Section 1 — Key Concepts in Biology

Page 2 — Cells

Warm-Up

These cells have a nucleus. — Eukaryotic cells

These often have plasmid DNA. — Prokaryotic cells

These cells can be bacteria. — Prokaryotic cells

1 a)

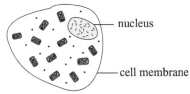

[2 marks — 1 mark for each correct label.]

b) Cell membrane — controls what goes in and out of the cell *[1 mark]*.

Nucleus — controls what the cell does / contains DNA *[1 mark]*.

Mitochondria — where most respiration happens *[1 mark]*.

c) E.g. ribosomes / cytoplasm *[1 mark]*

d) Any two from: e.g. there is no cell wall. / There is no large vacuole. / There are no chloroplasts. *[2 marks — 1 mark for each correct answer.]*

Page 3 — Specialised Cells

1 a) To carry the male DNA to the egg *[1 mark]*.

b) It allows the sperm to swim to the egg *[1 mark]*.

c) E.g. mitochondria. These release the energy needed for swimming. / Acrosome. This stores enzymes which digest the membrane of the egg. / A haploid nucleus. This means that the cell resulting from fertilisation will have the right number of chromosomes. *[2 marks — 1 mark for a correct feature and 1 mark for a correct explanation of this feature.]*

2 a) $56 \div 2 = 28$ *[1 mark]*

Egg cells are haploid, which means that there are half the number of chromosomes in the nucleus as in a normal body cell. So all you have to do is divide the number of chromosomes in a body cell by 2.

b) To stop more sperm getting in *[1 mark]*, so that only one sperm can fertilise the egg *[1 mark]*.

c) It contains lots of nutrients to feed the embryo *[1 mark]*.

Page 4 — Microscopy

1 a) i) $\times 4$ *[1 mark]*

Remember, you should always start with the objective lens with the lowest magnification — this makes it easier to get your specimen into view.

ii) They bring the sample into focus by moving the stage up and down *[1 mark]*.

iii) She should select the $\times 10$ or $\times 40$ objective lens *[1 mark]* and use the adjustment knobs to bring the sample back into focus *[1 mark]*.

b) Any two from: e.g. she should use a sharp pencil. / She should not colour or shade her drawing. / She should label her drawing with straight, uncrossing lines. / She should include the magnification used and a scale. / Her drawing should take up at least half of the space available. *[2 marks — 1 for each correct answer.]*

c) E.g. the image viewed with the electron microscope would be more detailed *[1 mark]*.

Page 5 — More Microsc

Warm-up

4.9 nm, 6 µm, 5 mm

1 a) D *[1 mark]*

Remember, total magnification = eyep magnification. $10 \times 100 = 1000$.

b) C *[1 mark]*

The height of the cell is about 2 and a half times the length of the scale bar. $10 \ \mu m \times 2.5 = 25 \ \mu m$

2 magnification = image size ÷ real size

$4 \div 0.01 = \times 400$ *[2 marks for the correct answer, otherwise 1 mark for the correct calculation]*

Page 6 — Enzymes

1 a) active site *[1 mark]*

b) B *[1 mark]*

2 a) A: carbohydrase *[1 mark]*

B: protein *[1 mark]*

C: amino acids *[1 mark]*

b) In order for an enzyme to catalyse a reaction, the substrate must fit into the enzyme's active site *[1 mark]*. Carbohydrates are the wrong shape to fit / do not fit a protease's active site *[1 mark]*.

Page 7 — Factors Affecting Enzyme Activity

1 At first, as substrate concentration increases, the rate of the reaction **increases**. Then when all the active sites are **full**, increasing the substrate concentration **doesn't change** the rate of the reaction. *[3 marks — 1 mark for each correct answer.]*

2 a) As temperature increases, rate of reaction increases *[1 mark]*.

b) E.g. 33°C *[1 mark — accept any answer between 31-34 °C]*.

For this question, you need to find the highest point on the graph, and then draw a straight line down to the temperature axis. Then you can just read off the temperature from where your line crosses the axis.

c) The temperature is too high *[1 mark]*, so the enzyme has been denatured / has changed shape so that the substrate no longer fits in the active site *[1 mark]*. This means the enzyme will no longer catalyse the reaction *[1 mark]*.

Page 8 — More on Enzyme Activity

1 a) 120 s *[1 mark]*

b) E.g. $1000 \div 120 = 8.33... = \textbf{8.3 s}^{-1}$ (2 s.f.) / $1 \div 120 = 0.00833... = \textbf{0.0083 s}^{-1}$ (2 s.f.)

[2 marks for a correct answer, otherwise 1 mark for a correct calculation.]

There's more than one way you could get the answer here. You should get full marks for using any correct calculation using any correct method in the exam.

c) Any two from: e.g. the temperature of the solutions / the concentration of starch solution / the volume of starch and amylase solution added to the test tube / the concentration of amylase / the volume of starch and amylase solution added to the iodine solution / the volume of iodine solution in the wells *[2 marks — 1 mark for each correct answer.]*

d) E.g. test the solutions more frequently (e.g. every 10 seconds) *[1 mark]*.

Page 9 — Diffusion, Osmosis and Active Transport

Warm-up

Diffusion is the movement of molecules from a higher to a lower concentration, so you have to draw the arrow going from the 1.5% solution to the 0.2% solution.

1 a) C *[1 mark]*
Remember, osmosis involves the movement of water molecules (so the answer isn't option B or D) across a partially permeable membrane (so the answer isn't option A).

b) Osmosis is the movement of **water** molecules across a partially permeable membrane from a **less** concentrated solution to a **more** concentrated solution. *[3 marks — 1 mark for each correct answer.]*

2 The mineral ions are at a higher concentration inside the cell than outside it *[1 mark]* so need to be moved into the cell against the concentration gradient *[1 mark]*.

Pages 10-11 — Investigating Osmosis

1 a) % change in mass
= ((final mass − initial mass) ÷ initial mass) × 100
= ((9.3 − 10) ÷ 10) × 100 = −0.07 × 100 = **−7%** *[2 marks for the correct answer, otherwise 1 mark for the correct calculation]*

b) i) Beaker 4 *[1 mark]* because the % change in mass should be negative at this concentration of sucrose solution *[1 mark]*.

ii) He should repeat the experiment again at a concentration of 0.7 M *[1 mark]*.

c) Beakers: 1 and 2 *[1 mark]*.
Reason: the cylinders in these two beakers increased in mass *[1 mark]*.

2 a) Any two from: e.g. the volume of sucrose solution the student puts in the Visking tubing. / The volume of sucrose solution the student puts in the beaker. / The temperature the beaker is kept at. / The size of the Visking tubing *[2 marks]*.

b) stayed the same *[1 mark]*.

c) The solution in the Visking tubing is less concentrated than the solution in the beaker *[1 mark]*.
Water molecules will move by osmosis from a less concentrated solution (where there are lots of water molecules) to a more concentrated solution (where there are fewer water molecules).

d) The water concentration of the solutions in the Visking tubing and the beaker will have become the same *[1 mark]*, so there will be no overall movement of water molecules *[1 mark]*.

Section 2 — Cells and Control

Page 12 — Mitosis

1 a) prophase — The membrane around the nucleus breaks down. *[1 mark]*
telophase — Membranes form around each new set of chromosomes. *[1 mark]*

b) The new cells are diploid *[1 mark]*.
The new cells are identical to each other *[1 mark]*.
The cells are diploid because they contain two copies of each chromosome (just like the original cell). They each contain exactly the same DNA as each other, meaning they are identical.

2 a) The cell makes a copy of its DNA *[1 mark]* and copies some of its subcellular structures *[1 mark]*.

b) anaphase *[1 mark]*
It's anaphase because you can see that each chromosome has split in half, and the two halves are being pulled to opposite ends of the cell.

Page 13 — Cell Division and Growth

1 a) Cell differentiation is how a cell changes to become specialised for its job *[1 mark]*.

b) cell division *[1 mark]*, cell elongation *[1 mark]*

2 a) 50th *[1 mark]*

b) At 10 months the child is in the 91st percentile.
91 − 50 = **41 percentiles** *[2 marks for the correct answer, or 1 mark for 91st percentile.]*

Page 14 — Stem Cells

Warm-Up
differentiate, early human embryos, any cell type

1 a) meristem tissue *[1 mark]*
For this question it's no good writing 'the tips of roots' or 'the tips of shoots' — you've been asked to name the tissue that produces stem cells, not give its location within a plant.

b) D *[1 mark]*

2 a) Stem cells are undifferentiated cells *[1 mark]*.

b) i) E.g. embryonic stem cells can produce any kind of specialised cell *[1 mark]*, whereas adult stem cells can only produce certain types of specialised cell *[1 mark]*.

ii) E.g. some people think embryos shouldn't be used as they're potential human lives *[1 mark]*.

c) E.g. the stem cells may divide uncontrollably in the patient and form a tumour. / The stem cells may contain a virus which could be passed on to the patient. / The patient's immune system may reject (try to fight off) the stem cells *[1 mark]*.

Pages 15-16 — The Nervous System

1 B *[1 mark]*
Remember, a nervous response always follows the same pathway, starting with a receptor and ending with an effector. The neurones are always in the same order too (sensory, relay, then motor).

2 a) myelin sheath *[1 mark]*

b) 0.09 × 1000 = **90 μm** *[1 mark]*

c) Dendrites carry nervous impulses towards the cell body of the motor neurone *[1 mark]*. The axon carries nervous impulses away from the cell body *[1 mark]*.

d) If a motor neurone is damaged, nervous impulses won't be able to pass between the CNS *[1 mark]* and the effector which carries out the response *[1 mark]*.

3 a) mean = (25 + 20 + 15) ÷ 3 = 60 ÷ 3 = **20 mm** *[2 marks for correct answer, otherwise 1 mark for correct working.]*

b) B *[1 mark]*.
From this experiment, the student doesn't have enough information to make any of the other conclusions, because they haven't measured any other parts of the body. But they can compare two of the parts of the body that they have measured.

c) Any value between 5 and 20 mm *[1 mark]*
The cheek is less sensitive than the palm, but more sensitive than the back of the hand — so the mean distance between toothpicks for the cheek should be between the values for the palm and the back of the hand.

d) E.g. the person being tested would be able to see how many toothpicks were touching their skin *[1 mark]*.

Page 17 — Synapses and Reflexes

Warm-up

Dropping a hot plate.

1   A *[1 mark]*

2 a)   To reduce the chance of the hand being injured by the flame. / To quickly move the hand away from the flame. *[1 mark]*

   b)   Level 0:   There is no relevant information. *[No marks]*

             Level 1:   There is some description of the pathway of the reflex, but there is little detail and information is missing. The points made are basic and not linked together. *[1 to 2 marks]*

             Level 2:   There is some description of the pathway of the reflex, but some detail is missing. Some of the points made are linked together. *[3 to 4 marks]*

             Level 3:   There is a clear and detailed description of the pathway of the reflex. The points made are well-linked and the answer has a clear and logical structure. *[5 to 6 marks]*

Here are some points your answer may include:

The stimulus is detected by receptors in the hand.

The receptors send electrical impulses along a sensory neurone in the arm.

When the impulses reach the synapse at the end of the sensory neurone, chemicals called neurotransmitters are released.

The neurotransmitters move across the synapse and set off new electrical impulses in a relay neurone (in the CNS).

The impulses reach another synapse, and neurotransmitters are released.

The neurotransmitters move across the synapse and set off new electrical impulses in a motor neurone.

Impulses are sent along the motor neurone to the effector, a muscle.

The muscle contracts / The effector produces a response and the hand is moved away from the flame.

Don't forget to use the diagram for help in this question — if you work round it bit by bit, it'll help you to get your answer in the right order.

Section 3 — Genetics

Page 18 — Sexual Reproduction and Meiosis

1   female — egg *[1 mark]*

        male — sperm *[1 mark]*

2 a)   C *[1 mark]*

   b)   D *[1 mark]*

   c)   zygote *[1 mark]*

Page 19 — DNA

1 a)   All of an organism's DNA *[1 mark]*.

   b)   A section of DNA that codes for a particular protein *[1 mark]*.

   c)   It is stored as chromosomes *[1 mark]*, which are long, coiled-up molecules of DNA *[1 mark]*.

2 a)   X = T/thymine *[1 mark]*, Y = G/guanine *[1 mark]*

   b)   A double helix is a double stranded spiral *[1 mark]*.

   c)   It is made up of lots of repeating units (nucleotides) *[1 mark]*.

Page 20 — Genetic Diagrams

Warm-Up

alleles, homozygous, multiple genes

1 a)

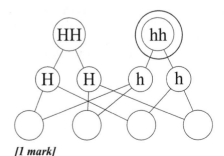

[1 mark]

   b)   A *[1 mark]*

   c)   The offspring all have short hair *[1 mark]*.

All the offspring have the genotype Hh. This means they all have the dominant allele (H), so they all have short hair.

Page 21 — More Genetic Diagrams

1 a)

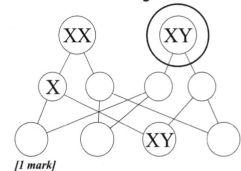

[1 mark]

   b)

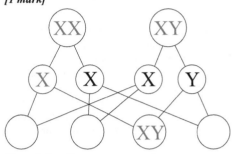

[1 mark for all gametes correct]

   c)

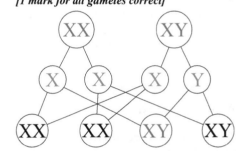

[1 mark if all the offspring genotypes are correct]

   d)   50 : 50 / 2: 2 / 1 : 1 *[1 mark]*

2 a)

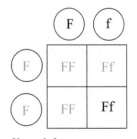

[1 mark for correct genotypes of gametes.
1 mark for correct genotype of offspring.]

   b)   half / 1 in 2 *[1 mark]*

   c)   none / 0 *[1 mark]*

Remember, cystic fibrosis is caused by a recessive allele, so two copies of the allele are needed for an individual to have it. None of the offspring in the Punnett square have two copies, so none of them have it.

Page 22 — Variation

1   mutations *[1 mark]*, sexual reproduction *[1 mark]*

2   E.g. flower shape / leaf shape / the size of the leaves/flowers / flower colour *[1 mark]*.

3   The difference in weight must be caused by the environment *[1 mark]*, because the twins have exactly the same genes *[1 mark]*

In this case, the environment can mean the amount of food each twin eats or the amount of exercise they each do.

Page 23 — *Mutations and The Human Genome Project*

1 a) C *[1 mark]*

  b) A single mutation usually has **no** *[1 mark]* effect on an organism's phenotype. Very rarely, a single mutation will have **a large** *[1 mark]* effect on an organism's phenotype.

2 How to grade your answer:

Level 0:	There is no relevant information. *[No marks]*
Level 1:	There is some information about how knowing the functions of genes could have benefits in medicine. The points made are basic and not linked together. *[1 to 2 marks]*
Level 2:	There is some discussion of how knowing the functions of genes could have benefits in medicine. Some of the points made are linked together. *[3 to 4 marks]*
Level 3:	There is a clear and detailed discussion of how knowing the functions of genes could have benefits in medicine. The points made are well-linked and the answer has a clear and logical structure. *[5 to 6 marks]*

Here are some points your answer may include:

Genes that increase a person's risk of getting a disease may be identified in an individual's genome. This means that the disease can be predicted in individuals. Steps can then be taken to reduce the risk of the disease from developing in those individuals.

Genes that cause genetic disorders may be identified in an individual. If genes for a particular genetic disorder are identified early, then treatment for the disorder can also be started early.

People with particular genes may react differently to different drugs. If a doctor knows what genes an individual has, they could choose the best drug for that individual. Scientists may also be able to develop better drugs for people with particular genes.

Section 4 — Natural Selection and Genetic Modification

Pages 24-25 — *Natural Selection and Evidence for Evolution*

Warm-up

Charles Darwin

1 a) Because of differences in their genes *[1 mark]*.

  b) Any two from: e.g. predators / competition for resources / disease *[2 marks — 1 mark for each correct answer]*.

2 a) Going down the table: 4, 2, 1, 3 *[2 marks for all four stages in the correct order, otherwise 1 mark for two stages in the correct order.]*

  b) Because antibiotic resistance is an adaptation to a selection pressure (the presence of antibiotics) *[1 mark]* and, as a result, it becomes more common in a population over time *[1 mark]*.

3 a) E.g. volume of nutrient broth solution / volume of ampicillin solution *[1 mark]*.

  b) E.g. use a pipette to transfer some of strain A to one bottle with ampicillin in it and one bottle without ampicillin *[1 mark]*. Use a different pipette to transfer some of strain B to one bottle with ampicillin and one bottle without ampicillin *[1 mark]*. Put lids on all of the bottles and store them all at the same temperature for a few days *[1 mark]*. Observe each bottle to see if the nutrient broth solution has gone cloudy *[1 mark]*.

  c) E.g. if strain B is resistant to ampicillin, it is important that it is not allowed to escape into the general population, so it must be disposed of properly. / The bacteria used may pose a health risk to humans if not disposed of properly. / If the antibiotic used is not disposed of properly it may escape into the environment, where other bacteria may develop resistance to it *[1 mark]*.

Pages 26-27 — *Fossil Evidence for Human Evolution*

Warm-up

apes, legs, feet, evolution

1 a)

[1 mark]

  b) 4.4 – 1.6 = **2.8 million years** *[1 mark]*

2 a) D *[1 mark]*

  b) Any two from: e.g. Turkana Boy had longer legs than Ardi or Lucy. / Turkana Boy had shorter arms than Ardi or Lucy. / Turkana Boy had a larger brain size than Ardi or Lucy. / The structure of Turkana Boy's legs were more suitable to walking upright than those of Ardi or Lucy.
[2 marks — 1 mark for each correct answer.]

3 Specimen 2 *[1 mark]*, because it has the smallest brain size (and human brain size has increased over time) *[1 mark]*.

4 a) It is in the deepest layer of rock *[1 mark]* and the deeper the rock the fossil is found in, the older it is likely to be *[1 mark]*.

  b) B *[1 mark]*. It is in the top layer of rock, which means it was the most recently made *[1 mark]* and is therefore likely to be the most complex *[1 mark]*.

Page 28 — *Classification*

Warm-up

True, False, True

1 a) plants, animals, fungi, prokaryotes and protists *[1 mark]*

  b) D *[1 mark]*

Remember, a species is the smallest group in the five kingdom classification system. Genus is the next smallest group.

2 a) Archaea *[1 mark]*, Bacteria *[1 mark]*

  b) Because genetic analysis *[1 mark]* showed that some members of the prokaryote kingdom were less closely related than first thought *[1 mark]*.

Page 29 — *Selective Breeding*

1 a) When humans choose which plants or animals are going to breed *[1 mark]*.

  b) B and C *[1 mark]*

  c) E.g. selectively bred organisms are more likely to have health problems caused by their genes *[1 mark]*. It's less likely that organisms will have resistance alleles for any new diseases *[1 mark]*.

2 From the existing stock, organisms that have the required characteristic are selected and bred together *[1 mark]*. The best of the offspring are selected and bred together *[1 mark]*. This process is continued over several generations *[1 mark]*.

Page 30 — *Genetic Engineering*

1 a) Genetic engineering involves changing an organism's genome *[1 mark]* to give it new and useful characteristics *[1 mark]*.

  b) C *[1 mark]*

2 a) E.g. it can be hard to predict how changing an animal's genome will affect the animal. / Many genetically modified embryos don't survive. / Some genetically modified animals suffer from health problems later in life *[1 mark]*.

  b) E.g. genes used in genetic engineering may get out into the environment. / Some people worry that GM crops might have a negative effect on food chains/human health *[1 mark]*.

3 a) To find out whether a GM crop affects the number of wild flowers growing in a nearby area *[1 mark]*.

  b) E.g. they could repeat their experiment with other meadows *[1 mark]*.

Section 5 — Health, Disease & the Development of Medicines

Page 31 — Health and Disease
Warm-up
Chalara ash dieback — fungus, Tuberculosis — bacterium, Malaria — protist, Cholera — bacterium
1 a) Health is a state of complete physical, mental and social well-being *[1 mark]*, and not merely the absence of disease or infirmity *[1 mark]*.
  b) A communicable disease can be spread between individuals, whereas a non-communicable disease can not *[1 mark]*.
2 a) E.g. it is spread through the air when infected individuals cough or sneeze *[1 mark]*.
  b) E.g. coughing/lung damage *[1 mark]*.
  c) E.g. infected individuals should avoid crowded public spaces *[1 mark]*. / Good hygiene should be practiced by the infected person *[1 mark]*. / The infected person should sleep alone *[1 mark]*.

Page 32 — STIs
1 a) B *[1 mark]*
  b) By sexual contact *[1 mark]*.
  c) Because Chlamydia often does not cause any symptoms *[1 mark]*.
  d) E.g. using a condom during sex / avoiding sexual contact *[1 mark]*.
2 a) The immune system is involved in fighting off diseases, so people with AIDS are less able to fight off other communicable diseases *[1 mark]*.
  b) HIV is spread via bodily fluids, including blood *[1 mark]* and sharing a needle could mean that infected blood is passed from one drug-user to the other *[1 mark]*.

Page 33 — Fighting Disease
1 White blood cells called **lymphocytes** *[1 mark]* produce proteins that lock onto **antigens** *[1 mark]* on the surface of pathogens. The proteins produced by white blood cells are called **antibodies** *[1 mark]*. They will each target **one type** *[1 mark]* of pathogen.
2 How to grade your answer:
Level 0: There is no relevant information. *[No marks]*
Level 1: There is a brief mention of one or two defences which reduce the number of pathogens entering the body. The points made are basic and not linked together. *[1 to 2 marks]*
Level 2: There is some explanation of how at least three of the body's defences reduce the number of pathogens entering the body. Some of the points made are linked together. *[3 to 4 marks]*
Level 3: There is a full and clear explanation of how at least four defences reduce the number of pathogens entering the body. The points made are well-linked and the answer has a clear and logical structure. *[5 to 6 marks]*
Here are some points your answer may include:
Physical barriers include the skin, mucus and cilia.
The skin stops pathogens entering the body.
If the skin is damaged then the blood clots at the wound. This seals the cut and keeps pathogens out.
The airways secrete mucus to trap pathogens. The mucus is then pushed up to the back of throat by cilia which line the airways. The mucus containing the pathogens can then be swallowed. This reduces the number of pathogens entering the airways.
Chemical barriers include acid in the stomach and lysozyme produced in the eyes.
The stomach produces hydrochloric acid, which kills pathogens that have been swallowed.
Lysozyme produced in the eyes kills bacteria on the surface of the eye.

Page 34 — Memory Lymphocytes and Immunisation
Warm-up
To make it less likely they get ill in the future.
1 a) C *[1 mark]*
  b) E.g. by producing antibodies / by producing memory lymphocytes *[1 mark]*.
2 Antibody production after infection in the immunised child happens much faster than in the unimmunised child *[1 mark]* and more antibodies are also produced *[1 mark]*.

Page 35 — Antibiotics and Other Medicines
1 D *[1 mark]*
2 a) D *[1 mark]*
In preclinical trials, animals are used to test the drug on a whole body or multiple body systems, so the animal needs to be alive. You wouldn't want to test on humans at this stage, just in case the drug is dangerous.
  b) E.g. how toxic it is *[1 mark]*, the dose at which it works best *[1 mark]*
  c) A substance that's like the drug being tested but doesn't do anything *[1 mark]*.
  d) So that doctors are able to compare the two groups *[1 mark]* to see if the drug makes a real difference to their condition *[1 mark]*.
  e) A trial in which neither the doctors nor the patients know who is receiving the drug and who is receiving the placebo *[1 mark]*.

Pages 36-37 — Non-Communicable Diseases
1 C *[1 mark]*
2 a) E.g. a diet high in fat and sugar *[1 mark]*, not getting enough exercise *[1 mark]*.
  b) When the liver breaks down alcohol, the products released can damage liver tissue *[1 mark]*.
  c) E.g. cardiovascular disease / lung disease / cancer *[1 mark]*.
3 E.g. they may reduce the number of people able to work, which may affect the amount of money in a country *[1 mark]*.
4 a) Similarity: E.g. the rate of obesity and the rate of diabetes both increased overall / show a positive correlation *[1 mark]*. Difference: E.g. the rate of diabetes increased every year whereas there were periods when the rate of obesity decreased or stayed the same *[1 mark]*.
  b) E.g. a correlation between the prevalence of obesity and the number of people with diabetes doesn't show that one causes the other. / Figure 1 shows that the percentage of people with obesity fell between 2015 and 2016, while the number of people with diabetes increased in the same year, which contradicts the student's statement. / The student is only comparing data for seven years — it may be that the trend is not present over a longer period of time *[1 mark]*.

Answers

Page 38 — Measures of Obesity

1 a)   C, D *[1 mark]*
  b)   1 *[1 mark]*
Only patient E has a BMI within the normal range of 18.5 - 24.9. All the other patients have BMIs outside of this range and so don't have a healthy BMI.
2 a)   170 cm = 1.70 m
     BMI = 73.5 ÷ 1.70^2
     = **25.4 kg m^{-2}** (3 s.f.) *[2 marks for correct answer, otherwise 1 mark for height = 1.70 m]*
  b)   91 ÷ 84 = **1.1** (2 s.f.) *[1 mark]*

Page 39 — Treatments for Cardiovascular Disease

Warm-up
heart, blood vessels (in any order)
1 a)   A *[1 mark]*
  b)   E.g. antihypertensives / anticoagulants *[1 mark]*.
2 a)   E.g. Stents *[1 mark]* keep arteries open, letting blood flow to the heart muscles *[1 mark]*. / Coronary bypass surgery *[1 mark]* allows blood to flow around a blocked artery *[1 mark]*. / A heart transplant *[1 mark]* replaces a diseased heart with a healthy heart from another person *[1 mark]*.
  b)   E.g. the patient could develop an infection after the surgery / lose a lot of blood *[1 mark]*.

Section 6 — Plant Structures and Their Functions

Page 40 — Photosynthesis

1 a)   E.g. algae *[1 mark]*
  b)   **carbon dioxide** *[1 mark]* + water ⟶ glucose + **oxygen** *[1 mark]*
  c)   A *[1 mark]*
2 a)   6 *[1 mark]*
  b)   The rate of photosynthesis increases as light intensity increases *[1 mark]*.

Page 41 — Transport in Plants

Warm-up
A: phloem tube
B: xylem tube
1 a) i)   E.g. sucrose *[1 mark]*
    ii)   E.g. water *[1 mark]*, mineral ions *[1 mark]*
  b)   C *[1 mark]*
2   It gives the roots a large surface area *[1 mark]*, for absorbing water and mineral ions from the soil *[1 mark]*.

Page 42 — Transpiration and Stomata

1 a)   The process by which water is lost from a plant is called **transpiration** *[1 mark]*. It is caused by the **evaporation** *[1 mark]* and diffusion of water from a plant's surface. The water loss creates a slight shortage of water in the plant, so more water is drawn up from the **roots** *[1 mark]*.
  b)   mineral ions *[1 mark]*
2 a)   X: stomata *[1 mark]*
     Y: guard cells *[1 mark]*
  b)   When these cells are swollen, the stomata are open *[1 mark]* and water can diffuse out of the plant *[1 mark]*. When these cells are limp, the stomata are closed *[1 mark]* and very little water can escape *[1 mark]*.

Page 43 — Transpiration Rate

1   Transpiration is **slower** *[1 mark]* in darker conditions. This is because stomata are **closed** *[1 mark]* in the dark. A warmer temperature leads to a **faster** *[1 mark]* transpiration rate because the water molecules in the leaves have **more** *[1 mark]* energy to move about.
2 a)   2.0 + 1.8 + 2.3 + 1.9 + 1.7 = 9.7
     9.7 ÷ 5 = 1.94 = **1.9** (2 s.f.) *[2 marks for correct answer, otherwise 1 mark for mean = 1.94]*
  b)   The greater the air flow around the plant, the greater the transpiration rate *[1 mark]*.
  c)   E.g. increasing air flow means that more water vapour is swept away from the plant / reduces the concentration of water vapour outside the leaves *[1 mark]*. This increases the rate of diffusion of water out of the leaves *[1 mark]*.

Section 7 — Animal Coordination, Control and Homeostasis

Page 44 — Hormones

1 a)   B *[1 mark]*
  b)   adrenaline *[1 mark]*
2 a)   D *[1 mark]*
  b)   C *[1 mark]*
  c)   It is carried in the blood *[1 mark]*.
  d)   Any two from: e.g. communication by hormones takes longer than communication by neurones. / Neurones act for a very short time, whereas hormones act for a long time. / Neurones act on a very precise area, whereas hormones act in a more general way. *[2 marks — 1 mark for each correct answer.]*

Page 45 — The Menstrual Cycle

1 a)   ovary *[1 mark]*
  b)   It causes the lining to thicken and grow *[1 mark]*.
  c)   ovulation *[1 mark]*
2 a)   C *[1 mark]* because that is when the level of progesterone starts to rise *[1 mark]*.
  b)   Her uterus lining will break down *[1 mark]* and menstruation (bleeding) will start *[1 mark]* because progesterone is needed to help maintain the uterus lining *[1 mark]*.

Page 46 — Contraception

Warm-Up
contraceptive injection, contraceptive patch
1 a)   They prevent sperm from reaching the egg *[1 mark]*.
  b)   (12 ÷ 600) × 100 = 2% *[1 mark]*.
     100% − 2% = **98%** *[1 mark]*.
You could also do this by subtracting 12 from 600 to get the number of women who don't get pregnant (588), and then working that out as a percentage ((588 ÷ 600) × 100 = 98%). Condoms often aren't used perfectly, so in real life, their percentage effectiveness is less than 98%.
  c)   E.g. some barrier methods protect against sexually-transmitted infections, whereas hormonal methods do not *[1 mark]*. Barrier methods do not have the same unpleasant side effects (e.g. headaches, mood changes) as hormonal methods can *[1 mark]*.
  d)   E.g. by using hormonal methods, a couple don't have to remember to use contraception every time they have sex *[1 mark]*. Hormonal methods are usually better at preventing pregnancy *[1 mark]*.
2   E.g. oestrogen *[1 mark]*. It stops eggs being released from the ovaries *[1 mark]*. / Progesterone *[1 mark]*. E.g. it stops sperm from reaching the egg by making the mucus in the cervix very thick *[1 mark]*.

Page 47 — Homeostasis — Control of Blood Glucose

Warm-Up
true, true, true
Homeostasis is keeping internal conditions constant. Blood glucose needs to be kept at a constant level, so it's not always true that anything that <u>decreases</u> the amount of glucose in the blood is homeostasis.

1 a) C *[1 mark]*
 b) Cells need the right conditions in order to work properly *[1 mark]*. Homeostasis maintains the right conditions for cells *[1 mark]*.
2 a) A *[1 mark]*
 b) insulin *[1 mark]*
 c) When there is too much glucose in the blood, some of it moves into the **liver**. The glucose is then changed into **glycogen** so it can be stored. *[2 marks — 1 mark for each correct answer.]*

Page 48 — Diabetes

1 a) D *[1 mark]*
 b) With insulin therapy / insulin injections *[1 mark]*.
2 a) i) the patient's height *[1 mark]*, the patient's mass *[1 mark]*
 ii) It should show whether the patient is obese *[1 mark]*. Being obese makes a person more likely to develop type 2 diabetes *[1 mark]*.
 b) Any two from: e.g. eat a healthy diet / get regular exercise / lose weight if needed *[2 marks — 1 for each correct answer]*.

Section 8 — Exchange and Transport in Animals

Page 49 — Exchange of Materials

Warm-Up
2 — tiger, 3 — bacterium , 1 — blue whale

1 a) Any two from: e.g. oxygen / mineral ions / water / food. *[2 marks — 1 mark for each correct answer]*
 b) E.g. carbon dioxide *[1 mark]*, urea *[1 mark]*
2 a) volume = 5 × 5 × 5 = **125 μm³** *[1 mark]*
The volume of a cube is just length × width × height.
 b) surface area of one face = 5 × 5 = 25 μm² *[1 mark]*
surface area of all six faces = 25 × 6 = **150 μm²** *[1 mark]*
 c) 3:1 *[1 mark]*
The surface area of the cube is 24 cm² and the volume is 8 cm³. This gives the cube a surface area to volume ratio of 24:8. To get the answer here, you need to simplify the ratio by dividing both sides by the volume.

Page 50 — Specialised Exchange Surfaces — the Alveoli

1 a) Oxygen moves from the air in the alveoli into the blood *[1 mark]*, carbon dioxide moves from the blood into the alveoli *[1 mark]*.
 b) diffusion *[1 mark]*
 c) The walls of the alveoli are thin *[1 mark]*.
 d) E.g. a good blood supply / a moist lining / a large surface area to volume ratio *[1 mark]*.

2

	Oxygen concentration	Carbon dioxide concentration
X	High	Low
Y	Low	**High**
Z	**High**	**Low**

[3 marks — 1 mark for each correct answer.]

Page 51 — Circulatory System — Blood

1 a)

	white blood cell	red blood cell
erythrocyte		✓
lymphocyte	✓	
phagocyte	✓	

[2 marks — 1 mark for each column correct.]
 b) B *[1 mark]*
 c) platelets *[1 mark]*
2 a) To carry oxygen from the lungs to all the cells in the body *[1 mark]*.
 b) It gives a large surface area for absorbing oxygen *[1 mark]*.
 c) This increases the space available for carrying oxygen in the cell *[1 mark]*.

Pages 52-53 — Circulatory System — Blood Vessels

Warm-up
A — artery, B — vein, C — capillary

1

Feature	Capillary	Artery	Vein
Elastic fibres in blood vessel walls		✓	
Large lumen			✓
Walls that are one cell thick	✓		
Valves			✓

[3 marks — 1 marks for each column in the table correctly filled in]

2 a) To carry blood close to every cell in the body *[1 mark]*, so that food and oxygen can be supplied to the cells and carbon dioxide/waste can be taken away *[1 mark]*.
 b) Because they have different functions *[1 mark]*. Arteries carry blood away from the heart at high pressure, while veins carry blood back to the heart at a lower pressure *[1 mark]*.
 c) They prevent blood from flowing backwards *[1 mark]*.
3 a) B *[1 mark]*.
 b) E.g. the wrong mass may have been used / the length may have been measured incorrectly / the mass carrier may have been removed *[1 mark]*.

Page 54 — Circulatory System — Heart

1 a) B *[1 mark]*
 b) E.g.

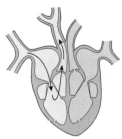

[1 mark for an arrow or arrows indicating the direction of blood flow into and out of the heart as shown.]

2 The wall of the left ventricle is thicker than the wall of the right ventricle *[1 mark]*. This is because it needs more muscle *[1 mark]*, because it pumps blood around the whole body and not just to the lungs as the right ventricle does *[1 mark]*.

3 Because the heart pumps blood around the body in two circuits *[1 mark]*. The first circuit pumps deoxygenated blood to the lungs to take in oxygen (and returns oxygenated blood to the heart) *[1 mark]*. The second circuit pumps oxygenated blood around all the other organs of the body (and returns deoxygenated blood to the heart) *[1 mark]*.

Page 55 — Heart Rate Calculations

Warm-up

heart rate, cardiac output, stroke volume

1 a) $57 \times 90 =$ **5130 cm^3 min^{-1}** *[1 mark]*
  b) heart rate = cardiac output ÷ stroke volume *[1 mark]*
    $= 5525 \div 85 =$ **65 bpm** *[1 mark]*
  c) beats per minute *[1 mark]*

Page 56 — Respiration

1 a)

Statement	Aerobic respiration	Anaerobic respiration
It transfers more energy.	✓	
It uses oxygen.	✓	
It can produce lactic acid.		✓

[2 marks — 1 mark for each column correct.]

  b) aerobic respiration *[1 mark]*
  c) glucose + oxygen → carbon dioxide + **water** *[1 mark]*
2 a) Respiration is a reaction carried out by **all** *[1 mark]* living organisms. Respiration is an **exothermic** *[1 mark]* reaction. It transfers energy **to** *[1 mark]* the environment.
  b) E.g. in metabolic reactions / to make larger molecules from smaller ones *[1 mark]*.

Pages 57-58 — Investigating Respiration

1 a) The snail released carbon dioxide as it respired *[1 mark]*.
  b) It will have decreased *[1 mark]* because the snail will have used up oxygen as it respired *[1 mark]*.
  c) E.g. the snail must have enough oxygen for two hours / the snail must not dry out *[1 mark]*.
  d) $(0.5 - 0.2) \div 2 = 0.3 \div 2$ *[1 mark]*
    $=$ **0.15 cm^3 h^{-1}** *[1 mark]*

The overall change in volume in two hours is 0.3 cm^3. To get the average rate of respiration per hour, you just divide this change in volume (0.3) by the number of hours (2).

2 a) Any one from: e.g. the mass of the peas in the flask / the size of the flask / the type of peas / the temperature outside of the flasks / the temperature of the peas at the start of the experiment *[1 mark]*.
  b) The reading of 31 °C in Flask 2 on Day 1 should be circled *[1 mark]*.
  c) The boiled peas will not germinate, so Flask 2 is included to show that the increase in temperature in Flask 1 is due to the peas germinating *[1 mark]*.

You get the mark here if you said something that meant the same as this, but said it in a different way — for example, you would get the mark for saying "Flask 2 was included as a control experiment."

  d) B *[1 mark]*.

The temperature of Flask 1 rose by 8 °C. As the student controlled other variables that could have affected the results, it must have been the germinating peas that released the heat energy in Flask 1. The student didn't directly measure how much the peas respired each day so you can't say that the last option is a valid conclusion based on what you know.

Section 9 — Ecosystems and Material Cycles

Page 59 — Ecosystems and Interdependence

1 community — all the organisms of different species in a habitat *[1 mark]*
  population — all the organisms of one species in a habitat *[1 mark]*
2 a) A community of organisms, along with all the non-living conditions in the area where they live *[1 mark]*.
  b) They depend on each other for things like food and shelter *[1 mark]*.
3 Both the ants and the tree benefit from the relationship *[1 mark]*. The ants have a source of food from the tree and the tree has defence against bacteria *[1 mark]*.

Page 60 — Factors Affecting Ecosystems

Warm-Up

'predators' and 'competition' should be circled.

1 a) C *[1 mark]*
  b) E.g. food *[1 mark]*, shelter *[1 mark]*
2 a) The number of rabbits might decrease *[1 mark]* because there would be more foxes eating them *[1 mark]*.
  b) If the number of rabbits decreases due to disease *[1 mark]*, then the number of foxes could decrease as there would be less food for them to eat *[1 mark]*.

Page 61 — Investigating Ecosystems

1 a) B and C *[1 mark]*
  b) A *[1 mark]*
2 a) mean = total number of organisms ÷ number of quadrats
    $= (26 + 23 + 18) \div 3 = 67 \div 3 = 22.33...$
    $=$ **22** (2 s.f.) *[2 marks for correct answer to 2 significant figures, otherwise 1 mark for mean = 22.33...]*
  b) total number of buttercups = mean per quadrat × total area
    $14 \times 1750 =$ **24 500** buttercups *[1 mark]*

The size of the quadrat is 1 m^2 so all you have to do is multiply the mean number of buttercups per quadrat by the total area of Area 1. If the quadrat had a different size, then you would first have to divide the area of the habitat by the size of the quadrat.

Pages 62-63 — Human Impacts on Biodiversity

1 a) Eutrophication is when too many **nutrients** *[1 mark]* enter a body of water. For example, it happens when **fertilisers** *[1 mark]* enter rivers from nearby fields. It leads to a build-up of **algae** *[1 mark]*. This blocks **light** *[1 mark]* from getting to the plants in the water below.
  b) B *[1 mark]*
2 a) The fish food will add extra nutrients to the surrounding water and eutrophication is caused by an excess of nutrients *[1 mark]*.
  b) The parasites might get out of the nets and infect wild animals in the surrounding waters *[1 mark]*. If this kills the wild animals, it could lead to a decrease in biodiversity around the nets *[1 mark]*.
  c) E.g. local fish populations could decrease *[1 mark]* because the escaped fish could eat a lot of food so that there's not enough left for the local populations *[1 mark]*.
3 a) E.g. the introduction of possums may have led to a reduction in the size of the populations of native birds *[1 mark]*, because there were fewer areas of shelter available *[1 mark]*.
  b) E.g. the possums may have eaten native wildlife *[1 mark]*.

4   How to grade your answer:
     Level 0: There is no relevant information. *[0 marks]*
     Level 1: There is a basic description of how reforestation
               programmes and conservation schemes help to
               maintain biodiversity and benefit local populations.
               The points made are basic and not linked together.
               [1-2 marks]
     Level 2: There is some description of how reforestation
               programmes and conservation schemes help to
               maintain biodiversity and benefit local populations.
               Some of the points made are linked together.
               [3-4 marks]
     Level 3: There is a clear and detailed description of how
               reforestation programmes and conservation
               schemes help to maintain biodiversity and benefit
               local populations. The points made are well-linked
               and the answer has a clear and logical structure.
               [5-6 marks]
     Here are some points your answer may include:
     <u>Reforestation programmes:</u>
     Reforestation is when deforested areas are replanted to create
     a new forest. This helps to restore biodiversity to the
     local area.
     Reforestation can create jobs for local people.
     It can also bring money to an area through ecotourism
     (environmentally-friendly tourism).
     <u>Conservation schemes:</u>
     Conservation schemes can help to protect biodiversity by
     preventing species from dying out.
     A species' natural habitat may be protected. This maintains
     biodiversity by making sure that species have a safe place
     to live.
     A species may be protected in safe areas outside of their
     natural habitat (e.g. animals can be protected in zoos).
     Some schemes may involve breeding organisms in safe areas.
     This maintains biodiversity by increasing the population sizes
     of the organisms.

Page 64 — The Carbon Cycle

1   A: photosynthesis *[1 mark]*
     B: eating *[1 mark]*
     C: respiration *[1 mark]*
2 a) Microorganisms break down dead matter *[1 mark]*. As they
     break it down, they release carbon dioxide back into the air
     through respiration *[1 mark]*.
  b) Plants take in carbon dioxide from the air during
     photosynthesis *[1 mark]*. They use the carbon in carbon
     dioxide to make carbon compounds *[1 mark]*.

Page 65 — The Water Cycle

Warm-Up

1   A *[1 mark]*
2 a) evaporation *[1 mark]*
  b) It provides fresh water for plants and animals *[1 mark]*.

Page 66 — The Nitrogen Cycle

1 a) When the crop is harvested and removed, the nitrogen isn't
     recycled back into the soil when it dies *[1 mark]*.
  b) E.g. crop rotation *[1 mark]*, fertilisers *[1 mark]*.
2 a) C *[1 mark]*
  b) D *[1 mark]* and E *[1 mark]*
  c) A *[1 mark]* and B *[1 mark]*

Section 10 — Key Concepts in Chemistry

Page 67 — Chemical Equations

Warm-up
1) True   2) False   3) True   4) True
1 a) sodium and water *[1 mark]*
  b) sodium hydroxide and hydrogen *[1 mark]*
2 a)

Ion	Element		
	Oxygen	Hydrogen	Nitrogen
Hydroxide	✓	✓	
Nitrate	✓		✓
Ammonium		✓	✓

[3 marks — 1 mark for each correct row]
  b) Elements: sulfur and oxygen *[1 mark]*
     Reason: The 'sulf-' tells you it contains sulfur and the '-ate'
     tells you it contains oxygen *[1 mark]*.

Page 68 — Balancing Equations

1

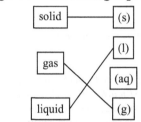

[3 marks — 1 mark for each correct answer]
2 a) D *[1 mark]*
  b) $4Na + O_2 \rightarrow 2Na_2O$
     [2 marks — 1 mark for each correct number]
3 a) $CaCO_{3(s)} + 2HCl_{(aq)} \rightarrow CaCl_2 \text{(aq)} + H_2O \text{(l)} + CO_2 \text{(g)}$
     *[2 marks — 1 mark for one or two correct symbols, 2 marks
     for three correct symbols]*
  b) $Ca + 2HCl \rightarrow CaCl_2 + H_2$
     *[2 marks — 1 mark for correct reactants and products and
     1 mark for balanced equation]*

Page 69 — Hazards and Risk

1

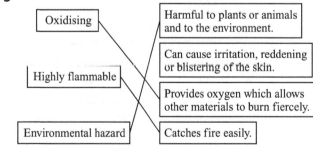

[3 marks — 1 mark for each correct answer]
2 a) B *[1 mark]*
  b) E.g. wear safety goggles / wear a lab coat / wear gloves
     [1 mark].
3 a) The gas can cause death if it's breathed in *[1 mark]*.
  b) E.g. the student should wear gloves / goggles / a lab coat
     [1 mark]. The student should carry out the experiment in a
     fume cupboard *[1 mark]*.

Page 70 — The History of the Atom

Warm-up

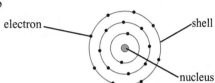

electron — shell

nucleus

1 a)   A *[1 mark]*
John Dalton described atoms as solid spheres at the start of the 1800s.
  b)   E.g. negatively charged electrons are stuck *[1 mark]* in a positively charged pudding *[1 mark]*.
2 a)   neutron *[1 mark]*
  b)   Scientists first thought that the positive charge was spread out through the whole atom *[1 mark]*. Then experiments showed that the positive charge is actually only found in the small nucleus at the centre of the atom *[1 mark]*. More experiments showed that the positive charge in the nucleus comes from small particles called protons *[1 mark]*.

Page 71 — The Atom

Warm-up
Protons and **neutrons** are found in the nucleus of an atom.
Electrons move around the nucleus in shells.
Compared to electrons, protons and neutrons are **heavy**.

1 a)

Particle	Relative Charge
Proton	+1
Neutron	0
Electron	−1

[3 marks — 1 mark for each correct answer]
  b)   1 *[1 mark]*
2 a)   nucleus *[1 mark]*
  b)   Protons have a relative charge of +1 *[1 mark]* and electrons have a relative charge of −1 *[1 mark]*. Because there is an equal number of protons and electrons in an atom, the positive charges on the protons cancel out the negative charges on the electrons *[1 mark]*.
Neutrons have a relative charge of zero, which means that they don't affect the overall charge of the atom (so you don't need to mention them here).

Page 72 — Atomic Number, Mass Number and Isotopes

1 a)   mass number = 39 *[1 mark]*
      atomic number = 19 *[1 mark]*
  b)   protons = 19 *[1 mark]*
      neutrons = mass number − atomic number
              = 39 − 19 = 20 *[1 mark]*
      electrons = 19 *[1 mark]*

2 a)

isotope	mass number	number of protons	number of neutrons	number of electrons
A	79	35	44	35
B	81	35	46	35

[2 marks — 1 mark for each correct row]
  b)   No they aren't isotopes *[1 mark]* because they have different atomic numbers/number of protons *[1 mark]*.

Page 73 — The Periodic Table

1 a)   By atomic number / proton number *[1 mark]*.
  b)   groups *[1 mark]*
  c)   3 *[1 mark]*
2   How to grade your answer:
      Level 0:   There is no relevant information *[No marks]*.
      Level 1:   There is a brief explanation of how Mendeleev arranged his table. The points made are basic and not linked together *[1 to 2 marks]*.
      Level 2:   There is some explanation of how Mendeleev arranged his table and how he predicted missing elements. Some of the points made are linked together *[3 to 4 marks]*.
      Level 3:   There is a clear and detailed explanation of how Mendeleev arranged his table and how he predicted missing elements. The points made are well-linked and the answer has a clear and logical structure *[5 to 6 marks]*.
      Here are some points your answer may include:
      Mendeleev placed the elements in order of atomic mass.
      He arranged the elements into groups based on how they (and their compounds) behaved.
      Some elements didn't quite fit the pattern.
      Mendeleev switched the order of some elements to keep those with the same properties together.
      He also left some gaps to keep elements with similar properties together.
      The gaps showed where elements that hadn't been discovered yet would go.
      Mendeleev predicted the properties of missing elements using the properties of other elements.

Page 74 — Electronic Configurations

1

Electron shell	Number of electrons it can hold
1st	2
2nd	8
3rd	8

[3 marks — 1 mark for each correct answer]
2 a)   C *[1 mark]*
  b)   The lowest energy shells / the shells closest to the nucleus *[1 mark]*.
3 a)   Chlorine: 2,8,7 *[1 mark]*
      Boron: 2,3 *[1 mark]*
  b)

You don't h... ... there is the ...

Page 75 - ...

1 a)   at...
  b)   1 ...
2

| A |
| D |
| X⁺ |
| Z²⁻ |

... non-metal from Group 7

[4 marks — 1 mark for each correct answer]
3 a)   zero *[1 mark]*
  b) K_2O *[1 mark]*

13

Page 76 — Ionic Bonding

1 a) Positive ions: cations *[1 mark]*
   Negative ions: anions *[1 mark]*
 b) Magnesium ion: Mg^{2+} *[1 mark]*
   Oxygen ion: O^{2-} *[1 mark]*
2 a)

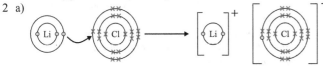

[1 mark for arrow showing electron transfer from Li to Cl, 1 mark for adding seven crosses and one dot to outer shell of the chloride ion, 1 mark for correct charges on both ions]
 b) electrostatic attraction / electrostatic force *[1 mark]*
 c) E.g. the particles in the compound are oppositely charged ions / have opposite charges / the bond is formed by electrons being transferred from one atom to another *[1 mark]*.

Page 77 — Ionic Compounds

Warm-up:
In an ionic compound, the particles are held together by **strong** forces of attraction. These forces are called ionic bonds and result in the particles bonding together to form **giant lattices**.

1 a) E.g.

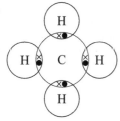

[1 mark for correct structure, with alternating ions]
You'd also get the marks if you labelled all the white circles as Br^- and all the grey circles as K^+.
 b) E.g. the diagram doesn't correctly represent the sizes of ions / it shows gaps between the ions *[1 mark]*.
2 a) giant ionic lattice *[1 mark]*
 b) Any two from: e.g. high melting point / high boiling point / many will dissolve in water / conduct electricity when molten / conduct electricity when dissolved in water / don't conduct electricity when solid *[2 marks — 1 mark for each correct answer]*.

Page 78 — Covalent Bonding

1 A covalent bond forms when atoms **share** *[1 mark]* a pair of **electrons** *[1 mark]*. Atoms form covalent bonds to get a full **outer** *[1 mark]* shell of electrons.
2 a) The bonds between the atoms in a molecule are stronger than the forces between the molecules *[1 mark]*.
 b) The bonds within the molecule do not break *[1 mark]*. The forces between the molecules are broken *[1 mark]*.
3

(diagram of methane CH_4 with H, C, H atoms)

[1 mark for the correct layout of atoms and shells, 1 mark for the correct number of electrons in each bond]

Page 79 — Giant Covalent Structures

1 a) A structure where all the atoms are bonded to each other by strong covalent bonds *[1 mark]*.
 b) The covalent bonds are very strong *[1 mark]*, so a lot of energy is needed to break them *[1 mark]*.
2 a) 4 *[1 mark]*
 b)

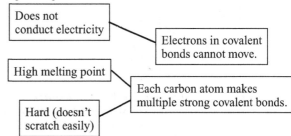

[2 marks if all three correct, otherwise 1 mark if one correct]
 c) In sheets/layers *[1 mark]*.
 d) Each carbon atom in graphite has one electron that's free to move *[1 mark]*. This means that graphite can conduct electricity, so it can be used as an electrode *[1 mark]*.

Page 80 — Polymers and Fullerenes

1 In a polymer lots of **small** *[1 mark]* units are joined together to form a **long** *[1 mark]* molecule.
2 a) Buckminsterfullerene: B *[1 mark]*
   Graphene: A *[1 mark]*
 b) Each carbon has one electron that's free to move so it can conduct electricity *[1 mark]*.
3 a) poly(ethene) *[1 mark]*
 b) covalent bonds *[1 mark]*

Page 81 — Metallic Bonding

1 E.g. metals have high melting/boiling points, whereas non-metals usually have low melting/boiling points *[1 mark]*. / Metals can conduct electricity whereas non-metals don't usually conduct electricity *[1 mark]*.
2 a) (free/delocalised) electrons *[1 mark]*
 b) There are strong forces of attraction between the positive metal ions and the (free/delocalised) negative electrons *[1 mark]*. These forces of attraction hold the atoms together in a regular pattern *[1 mark]*.
 c) Metallic bonds are very strong *[1 mark]* so lots of energy is needed to break them *[1 mark]*.
 d) The layers are able to slide over one another *[1 mark]*.

Page 82 — Conservation of Mass

1 $3.0 + 15.0 = $ **18 g** *[1 mark]*
2 a) $23.2 - 25.4 = $ **−2.2 g** *[1 mark]*
 b) E.g. the student is correct that no mass is lost or gained in a chemical reaction *[1 mark]*. The student isn't correct that the measurements must be wrong *[1 mark]*. Carbon dioxide gas has escaped from the conical flask *[1 mark]* so hasn't been counted in the final measurement *[1 mark]*.

Answers

Page 83 — Relative Masses

1 a) relative formula mass of HCl = 35.5 + 1 = **36.5** *[1 mark]*
  b) relative formula mass of Cl_2 = 35.5 + 35.5 = **71** *[1 mark]*

2

[3 marks — 1 mark for each correct answer]

3 a) relative formula mass of MgO = 24 + 16 = **40** *[1 mark]*
  b) relative amount of Mg = mass ÷ M_r = 48 ÷ 24 = 2
   ratio of Mg to MgO is 1:1, so relative amount of MgO is 2
   mass of MgO = relative amount × M_r = 2 × 40 = **80 g**
   [3 marks for correct answer, otherwise 1 mark for calculating relative amount of Mg and 1 mark for calculating relative amount of MgO.]
   You still get all the marks for this part if you got the answer to 3a) wrong, but used it correctly here.

Pages 84-85 — Calculating Empirical Formulas

Warm-up
The **empirical** formula tells you the **smallest** whole number ratio of atoms in a compound. You can work it out using the **molecular** formula for a compound.

1 A *[1 mark]*
The largest number that goes into both 2 and 4 is 2, so you need to divide by 2 to get the empirical formula.

2 D *[1 mark]*
The only molecular formula that has all the atoms in the same ratio as the empirical formula is D.

3 The largest number that goes into both 10 and 14 exactly is 2.
 B: 10 ÷ 2 = 5   H: 14 ÷ 2 = 7
 So the empirical formula of decaborane is B_5H_7 *[1 mark]*.

4 Relative mass of empirical formula is
 (A_r of C) + (2 × A_r of H) = 12 + (2 × 1) = 12 + 2 = 14
 M_r of Q ÷ M_r of empirical formula = 42 ÷ 14 = 3
 So to get the molecular formula, multiply the numbers of atoms in the empirical formula by 3:
 molecular formula = C_3H_6
 [3 marks for correct answer, otherwise 1 mark for finding the relative mass of the empirical formula and 1 mark for dividing the relative mass of the molecular formula by the relative mass of the empirical formula]

5 a) relative amount of H = 2 ÷ 1 = 2
   relative amount of O = 32 ÷ 16 = 2
   ratio H:O = 2:2 or 1:1
   So the empirical formula must be **HO**.
   [3 marks for correct answer, otherwise 1 mark for finding the relative amount of H and O and 1 mark for dividing by the smallest number]
  b) Relative mass of empirical formula is = (A_r of H) + (A_r of O)
   = 1 + 16 = 17
   M_r of X ÷ M_r of empirical formula = 34 ÷ 17 = 2
   So to get the molecular formula, multiply the numbers of atoms in the empirical formula by 2: molecular formula = H_2O_2.
   [3 marks for correct answer, otherwise 1 mark for finding the relative mass of the empirical formula and 1 mark for dividing the relative mass of the molecular formula by the relative mass of the empirical formula]

6 a) mass of O = 2.20 − 1.32 = **0.88 g** *[1 mark]*
  b) relative amount of Mg = 1.32 ÷ 24 = 0.055
   relative amount of O = 0.88 ÷ 16 = 0.055
   Dividing by the smallest number: Mg = 0.055 ÷ 0.055 = 1 and O = 0.055 ÷ 0.055 = 1.
   The ratio of Mg to O is 1:1, so the empirical formula is **MgO**.
   [3 marks for correct answer, otherwise 1 mark for finding the relative amount of Mg and O and 1 mark for dividing by the smallest number]

Page 86 — Concentration

Warm-up

Unit	Mass	Volume
g	✓	
cm^3		✓
dm^3		✓
kg	✓	

1 D *[1 mark]*
D is more concentrated as it has more solid dissolved in the same volume of water.

2 a) Volume of water = 400 ÷ 1000 = 0.4 dm^3
   Conc. of calcium chloride = 28 g ÷ 0.4 dm^3 = **70 g dm^{-3}**
   [2 marks for correct answer, otherwise 1 mark for using the correct equation]
  b) The concentration of a solution is the amount of a substance in a given volume of a solution *[1 mark]*.
  c) Mass = conc. × volume = 50 g dm^{-3} × 0.2 dm^3 = **10 g**
   [2 marks for correct answer, otherwise 1 mark for using the correct equation]

Section 11 — States of Matter and Mixtures

Page 87 — States of Matter

Warm-up
Particles in liquids are held in fixed positions by strong forces.

1 a) C *[1 mark]*
  b) The particles in a substance *[1 mark]*.
2 a) gas (most) → liquid → solid (least) *[1 mark]*
  b) In a solid the particles are held in fixed positions which means they have a fixed shape *[1 mark]*.

Page 88 — Changes of State

1 Process A: freezing *[1 mark]*
 Process B: melting *[1 mark]*
2 a) sodium chloride *[1 mark]*
At 900 °C, water would be a gas and copper would be a solid.
  b) Sodium chloride *[1 mark]* and water *[1 mark]*.
At 1500 °C, copper would be a liquid.
  c) A physical change doesn't change what the substance is *[1 mark]* whereas in a chemical change the atoms in the substances you start off with are rearranged to form different substances *[1 mark]*.

Page 89 — Purity

1 a) C *[1 mark]*
  b)

Substance	Pure	Mixture
Seawater		✓
Distilled water	✓	
Copper	✓	
Copper oxide	✓	

[4 marks — 1 mark for each correct answer]

2 a) The pure compound will have a single, sharp melting point *[1 mark]* whereas the mixture will melt gradually over a range of temperatures *[1 mark]*.
  b) melting point apparatus / water/oil bath and thermometer *[1 mark]*

Pages 90-92 — Separating Mixtures

1 a) **A**: Bunsen burner *[1 mark]*
   B: round bottom flask *[1 mark]*
   C: thermometer *[1 mark]*
   D: condenser *[1 mark]*
 b) C *[1 mark]*
2 a) Filtration is used to separate **insoluble** *[1 mark]* solids from **liquids** *[1 mark]*.
 b) C *[1 mark]*
3

Step	Order
The flask is heated slowly.	1
The first liquid is collected.	4
The heat of the flask is increased.	5
The substance with lowest boiling point evaporates and rises up the column.	2
The substance with lowest boiling point condenses and runs down the condenser.	3

[4 marks — 1 mark for each correct answer]

4 a) barium sulfate *[1 mark]*
 b) How to grade your answer:
   Level 0: Nothing written worthy of credit *[No marks]*.
   Level 1: A brief method is given, but there are steps missing. The points made are basic and not linked together *[1 to 2 marks]*.
   Level 2: A method is given, but it is lacking in detail, or steps are out of order. Some of the points made are linked together *[3 to 4 marks]*.
   Level 3: A clear and detailed method is given. The points made are well-linked and the answer has a clear and logical structure *[5 to 6 marks]*.
   Here are some points your answer may include:
   Gently heat the solution in an evaporating dish.
   Stop heating once some of the solvent has evaporated or when crystals start to form.
   Leave the solution to cool until crystals have formed.
   Put some filter paper in a funnel and place the funnel in a beaker.
   Pour the mixture into the filter paper.
   After all the liquid has passed through the filter paper leave the crystals to dry out.
5 a) In the first step, the temperature that the student heated the solution to was too high *[1 mark]*. Heating the mixture to 100 °C will cause both the ethanol and the water to evaporate *[1 mark]*.
 b) E.g. the student should heat the mixture to a temperature of between 78 °C and just under 100 °C. This will cause the ethanol in the mixture to evaporate, but not the water *[1 mark]*.
 c) Bismuth iodide is soluble in ethanol but not in water *[1 mark]*. If the student removed the water instead of the ethanol, the bismuth iodide would still be dissolved in the solution and could not be removed by filtration *[1 mark]*.
 d) The student should stop heating the solution when crystals start to form *[1 mark]*. They should then filter the crystals out of the solution and leave them in a warm place to dry *[1 mark]*.

Page 93 — Chromatography
Warm-up

1 a) To stop the solvent/ethanol from evaporating away *[1 mark]*.
 b) D *[1 mark]*
In paper chromatography, the solvent is the mobile phase and the solvent used in this experiment was ethanol.
 c) The different dyes move up the paper at different speeds so they form spots in different places *[1 mark]*.

Page 94 — Interpreting Chromatograms
1 a) water *[1 mark]*
 b) They only produce one spot on the chromatogram *[1 mark]*.
 c) C *[1 mark]*
 d) Repeat the experiment in different solvents *[1 mark]*. If it contains the reference substance, the spots on the chromatograms will have matching R_f values in each solvent *[1 mark]*.
 e) R_f = distance moved by substance ÷ distance moved by solvent
   $R_f = 9.0 ÷ 12.0 =$ **0.75**
   [2 marks for correct answer, otherwise 1 mark for correct working]

Page 95 — Water Treatment
Warm-up
Potable water is the same as drinking water — true.
Potable water can only be produced from fresh water found in rivers, streams and reservoirs — false.
Sea water can be made drinkable by distillation — true.
1 a) B *[1 mark]*
 b) You need to use pure water because normal water contains ions *[1 mark]* which could affect the reaction and give the experiment a false result *[1 mark]*.
2 a) filtration *[1 mark]*
 b) Chemicals are added *[1 mark]* which make small particles in the water clump together and settle at the bottom *[1 mark]*.
 c) It kills any harmful bacteria / microbes *[1 mark]*.

Section 12 — Chemical Changes

Page 96 — Acids and Bases
Warm-up
Substances with a pH of less than 7 are **acids**.
Substances with a pH of 7 are **neutral**.
1 a) beer *[1 mark]*
 b) pink *[1 mark]*
2 a) B *[1 mark]*
 b) A substance that reacts with an acid to form a salt and water *[1 mark]*.
 c) alkalis *[1 mark]*
 d) 0 *[1 mark]* – 14 *[1 mark]*

Page 97 — Neutralisation Reactions

1 a) e.g. pH meter / universal indicator / pH probe *[1 mark]*

  b)

[1 mark for points plotted correctly, 1 mark for smooth curve of best fit]

  c) E.g. to begin with, the pH increased slowly as the base was added *[1 mark]*. After 0.6 g of base was added, there was a more sudden increase in pH *[1 mark]*. The pH then continued to increase but more slowly *[1 mark]* until it stopped at pH 7 *[1 mark]*.

2 a) acid + base → salt + water *[1 mark]*

  b) $H^+ + OH^- \rightarrow H_2O$ *[1 mark]*

  c) 7 *[1 mark]*

Page 98 — Reactions of Acids

1 Hydrochloric acid — chloride
  Nitric acid — nitrate
  Sulfuric acid — sulfate *[2 marks for all three correct, otherwise 1 mark for 1 correct]*

2 a) water *[1 mark]*, carbon dioxide *[1 mark]*

  b) C *[1 mark]*

3 a) Test: bubble the gas through limewater *[1 mark]*.
     Observation: the limewater will go cloudy *[1 mark]*.

  b) hydrogen *[1 mark]*

Pages 99-100 — Making Soluble Salts

Warm-up
You should have circled sodium chloride, copper nitrate and zinc sulfate.

1 a) burette *[1 mark]*

  b) The indicator will change colour *[1 mark]*.

  c) E.g. so that there isn't any acid or alkali left over in the conical flask / so that the flask only contains water and the salt *[1 mark]*.

  d) E.g. so that the final product is pure / so that the product doesn't contain impurities of the indicator *[1 mark]*.

2 a) It will dissolve in water *[1 mark]*.

  b) All nitrates are **soluble** *[1 mark]* in water. Most chloride salts are soluble in water, except for silver chloride and **lead** *[1 mark]* chloride. Most **hydroxide** *[1 mark]* salts are insoluble in water.

  c) The zinc sulfate will dissolve *[1 mark]*.

3 Add copper oxide to sulfuric acid until the reaction stops/ the excess metal oxide sinks to the bottom *[1 mark]*. Filter the excess solid from the solution *[1 mark]*. Heat the copper sulfate solution to evaporate some of the water and then leave to cool *[1 mark]*. Filter and dry the crystals that form *[1 mark]*.

Page 101 — Making Insoluble Salts

1 D *[1 mark]*

2 a) iron hydroxide *[1 mark]*

  b) Add water to some iron nitrate in a test tube *[1 mark]*. Stopper the test tube and shake it *[1 mark]*.

  c) i) A precipitate would form *[1 mark]*.

    ii) To make sure all the precipitate is transferred from the beaker to the filter paper *[1 mark]*.

    iii) To make sure the final salt doesn't contain impurities of other ions *[1 mark]*.

Pages 102-104 — Electrolysis

1 a) A: power supply *[1 mark]*, B: wire *[1 mark]*, C: molten ionic compound *[1 mark]*, D: electrode *[1 mark]*

  b) So that toxic fumes aren't released into the room *[1 mark]*.

2 a) A *[1 mark]*

  b) In electrolysis, the anode is the **positive** *[1 mark]* electrode. **Negative** *[1 mark]* ions move to the anode. The cathode is the **negative** *[1 mark]* electrode. **Positive** *[1 mark]* ions move to the cathode.

3 a) An ionic compound *[1 mark]* that is a liquid or dissolved in water *[1 mark]*.

  b) lead and bromide *[1 mark]*

  c) lead bromide → lead + bromine *[1 mark]*

4 a) inert electrodes — oxygen gas and copper metal *[1 mark]*
     copper electrodes — copper and copper ions *[1 mark]*

  b) i) E.g. so that no copper sulfate solution was included in the measurements / so the measurements were accurate *[1 mark]*.

    ii) mass of negative electrode/cathode = 8.48 – 7.56 = **0.92 g** *[1 mark]*

  c) The movement of ions *[1 mark]*.

5 a) C *[1 mark]*

  b) Sodium is more reactive than hydrogen *[1 mark]*.

  c) chlorine *[1 mark]*

  d) sodium *[1 mark]* and chlorine *[1 mark]*

6 How to grade your answer:

Level 0: There is no relevant information. *[No marks]*

Level 1: The description of how copper is purified using electrolysis is vague, and misses out important details. The points made are basic and not linked together. *[1 to 2 marks]*

Level 2: Some description of how electrolysis can purify copper is given. The identity of the electrodes are correctly given, and some attempt is made to describe what happens to the copper during electrolysis. Some of the points made are linked together. *[3 to 4 marks]*

Level 3: There is a clear and detailed description of how electrolysis can be used to purify copper. The identity of the electrodes are correctly given, and there is a clear explanation of how the copper atoms and ions move during electrolysis. The points made are well-linked and the answer has a clear and logical structure. *[5 to 6 marks]*

Here are some points your answer may include:

The positive electrode/anode starts as a lump of impure copper.

The negative electrode/cathode starts as a thin piece of pure copper.

The electrolyte is copper sulfate solution.

Copper atoms from the impure positive electrode/anode form copper ions which dissolve in the solution.

The copper ions move towards the negative electrode/cathode.

At the negative electrode/cathode, the copper ions react to form pure copper.

The impurities from the positive electrode/anode sink to the bottom of the tank.

Section 13 — Extracting Metals and Equilibria

Page 105 — The Reactivity Series
1 a) copper *[1 mark]*
  b) potassium *[1 mark]*
2 a) Reduction is the loss of oxygen. *[1 mark]*
  b) Element: carbon *[1 mark]*.
    Reason: It gains oxygen during the reaction *[1 mark]*.
3 Oxidation is the reaction with/gain of oxygen *[1 mark]*. When a metal is burnt in air, the metal gains oxygen to form a metal oxide / an oxygen-containing product *[1 mark]*.

Page 106 — Reactivity of Metals
1 a) Metal A *[1 mark]*
  b) E.g. add the metal to the acid and watch how quickly bubbles are formed/see how quickly the metal dissolves *[1 mark]*.
2 a) calcium + water → calcium hydroxide + hydrogen *[1 mark]*
  b) Lithium, calcium, magnesium, copper *[2 marks for correct answer, otherwise 1 mark for 2 metals in the correct places]*
  c) E.g. use the same volume of water / use the same amount of metal / use the same surface area of metal *[1 mark]*.
  d) Magnesium chloride *[1 mark]* and copper *[1 mark]*
  e) A more reactive metal will displace a less reactive metal from its compound *[1 mark]*.

Page 107 — Extracting Metals Using Carbon
1 a) extraction *[1 mark]*
  b) Aluminium is **reactive** *[1 mark]*, so is found in the Earth's crust as an **ore** *[1 mark]*. Gold is **unreactive** *[1 mark]*, so is found in the Earth's crust as an **uncombined element** *[1 mark]*.
2 a) zinc *[1 mark]*
  b) Metal: calcium/potassium *[1 mark]*
    Reason: it is more reactive than carbon so will not be reduced by it *[1 mark]*.
3 Iron is extracted by reduction with carbon *[1 mark]*. Sodium is extracted using electrolysis *[1 mark]*. Iron is lower in the reactivity series / less reactive than carbon, and sodium is higher in the reactivity series / more reactive than carbon *[1 mark]*.

Page 108 — Extracting Metals Using Electrolysis
1 a) E.g. it is more reactive than carbon so cannot be reduced by it *[1 mark]*.
  b) E.g. electrolysis uses large amounts of electricity, which is expensive *[1 mark]*. There are also costs associated with melting magnesium *[1 mark]*.
2 a) molten aluminium *[1 mark]*
  b) It would make it less expensive *[1 mark]*.
Cryolite is added because it lowers the melting point of the ore. This means that less electricity is required to melt the ore, which makes the process cheaper.
  c) $2 Al_2O_3 \rightarrow 4 Al + 3 O_2$ *[1 mark for correct reactants and products, 1 mark for correct balancing]*

Page 109 — Recycling
1 B *[1 mark]*
2 a) Material B because less energy is needed to recycle it than A and C *[1 mark]*. Energy costs money *[1 mark]*.
  b) Material A is abundant so conserving it through recycling is not as important *[1 mark]*. The recycling of material A uses a lot of energy *[1 mark]*. Only a low level of energy is needed to extract material A *[1 mark]*.
  c) E.g. more fossil fuels will need to be burnt which will lead to air pollution/acid rain/climate change/higher greenhouse gas emissions. / High energy processes will use up lots of fossil fuels which are finite resources *[1 mark]*.
  d) Material: B
    Reason: it needs more energy to extract and less energy to recycle than material C *[both parts must be correct for 1 mark]*.

Pages 110-111 — Life Cycle Assessments
1 C *[1 mark]*
2 a) E.g. mining metals can damage the environment / extracting/processing metals uses lots of energy / extracting/processing metals causes pollution *[1 mark]*.
  b) E.g. the phone contains toxic materials that may be released if it is disposed of in landfill *[1 mark]*.
3 a) E.g. less waste is produced during the manufacture *[1 mark]*. They can be reused several times *[1 mark]*.
  b) Any two from: e.g. energy used in extraction / energy used in manufacture / pollutants produced during extraction / pollutants produced during manufacture *[2 marks — 1 mark for each correct answer]*.
4 a) E.g. glass bottles can be reused multiple times *[1 mark]*.
  b) The energy required for recycling cans and extracting aluminium from ore comes from burning fossil fuels, which releases greenhouse gases *[1 mark]*. As recycling cans uses less energy, it requires less burning of fossil fuels and therefore less greenhouse gases are produced *[1 mark]*.
You could also mention that it would preserve the supply of valuable raw materials, or that it would eliminate the environmental problems associated with mining.
  c) E.g. significant amounts of waste could be produced if the glass for recycling is contaminated *[1 mark]*.
  d) Any one from: e.g. how likely they are to be recycled / how easy it is to recycle them / the environmental costs of disposal if they are sent to landfill / their biodegradability *[1 mark]*

Pages 112-113 — Dynamic Equilibrium

Warm-up

Temperature: **450 °C**

Pressure: **200 atm**

Catalyst: **iron**

1 a) $N_2 + 3 H_2 \rightleftharpoons 2 NH_3$ *[1 mark]*

  b) Nitrogen — the atmosphere *[1 mark]*
  Hydrogen — natural gas *[1 mark]*

2 a) At dynamic equilibrium, the rates of the forward and the backward reaction are equal/the same *[1 mark]* and the relative concentrations of the reactants and products at equilibrium do not change *[1 mark]*.

  b) A closed system is a system where none of the reactants or products can escape *[1 mark]*.

  c) e.g. temperature/pressure/concentration of reactants *[1 mark]*

3 a) Line 1 represents the concentration of methanol *[1 mark]*. At the start of the reaction, there is no methanol present in the reaction mixture, but the concentration increases as the reaction takes place *[1 mark]*.

  b) The reaction reached equilibrium at time C *[1 mark]*. At time C, both lines are flat, meaning the concentrations of the reactants and the products are constant *[1 mark]*.

  c) Any one from: e.g. cooling/decreasing the temperature of the reaction mixture / increasing the pressure of the system / removing methanol to decrease the concentration of methanol present in the reaction mixture *[1 mark]*.

  d) E.g.

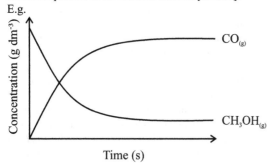

[1 mark for the correct curves, 1 mark for the correct labels]

It's also correct if your curves don't cross, as long as you show the concentration of carbon monoxide increasing and the concentration of methanol decreasing.

Section 14 — Groups in the Periodic Table

Page 114 — Group 1 — Alkali Metals

1 a) B *[1 mark]*

  b) They all have one electron in their outer shell / they have the same number of electrons in their outer shells *[1 mark]*.

2 a) sodium + water → **sodium hydroxide** + **hydrogen**
  [2 marks — 1 mark for each correct answer]

  b) Any one from: e.g. the sodium will move around the surface of the water / the sodium will fizz wildly / the sodium will decrease in size as it dissolves / the sodium will melt in the heat of the reaction *[1 mark]*.

  c) E.g. the outer electron of potassium is further away from the nucleus than the outer electron of sodium *[1 mark]*. This means the outer electron of potassium is less attracted to the nucleus *[1 mark]* and more easily lost *[1 mark]*.

  d) The alkali metals all have one outer electron *[1 mark]*, so losing one electron gives them a +1 ion with a stable electronic structure/full outer shell *[1 mark]*.

Pages 115 — Group 7 — Halogens

1 The Group 7 elements all have **seven** *[1 mark]* electrons in their outer shell. They can react to form ions with a **-1** *[1 mark]* charge. These ions are called **halides** *[1 mark]*.

2 a) damp blue litmus paper *[1 mark]*

  b) chlorine *[1 mark]*

3 a) bromine *[1 mark]*

  b) Chlorine is more reactive than bromine *[1 mark]*. This is because chlorine's outer shell is closer to the nucleus than bromine's *[1 mark]*. This means it's easier for chlorine to gain an electron when it reacts *[1 mark]*.

Pages 116-117 — Reactions of Halogens

Warm-up

Halogens react with hydrogen to form hydrogen halide: true

Hydrogen halides can dissolve in water: true

Hydrogen halides form alkaline solutions: false

1

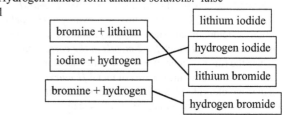

[3 marks — 1 mark for each correct answer.]

2 a) A displacement reaction is where a more reactive element displaces a less reactive element from a compound *[1 mark]*.

  b) chlorine water/potassium bromide — reaction *[1 mark]*
  iodine water/potassium bromide — no reaction *[1 mark]*
  bromine water/potassium chloride — no reaction *[1 mark]*
  chlorine water/potassium iodide — reaction *[1 mark]*

3 a) i) sodium bromide *[1 mark]*

   ii) potassium iodide *[1 mark]*

  b) $2Li + Cl_2 \rightarrow 2LiCl$
  [2 marks for all formulas correct and a correctly-balanced equation, otherwise 1 mark for correct formulas in an unbalanced equation]

  c) Product: magnesium bromide *[1 mark]*
  Reason: e.g. bromine and chlorine will react in similar ways because they're in the same Group / have the same number of electrons in their outer shells *[1 mark]*.

All of the halogens have similar reactions because they all have seven electrons in their outer shell. So you can predict that bromine and magnesium would also form a magnesium halide.

4 a) C *[1 mark]*

  b) Chlorine is more reactive than bromine and iodine *[1 mark]* so it can displace them from their compound and change the colour of the solution *[1 mark]*.

  c) chlorine + sodium astatide → **astatine** + **sodium chloride**
  [2 marks — 1 mark for each correct product]

Page 118 — Group 0 — Noble Gases

1 a) gases *[1 mark]*

  b) It has a stable electron arrangement / full outer shell of electrons *[1 mark]*.

2 a) Any value above −108 °C and below 25 °C *[1 mark]*.

Boiling point increases down the group, so radon will boil at a higher temperature than xenon. All the Group 0 elements are gases at room temperature, so radon must have a boiling point below 25 °C.

  b) density of argon = 1.78 kg m^{-3} *[1 mark]*
  density of krypton = 3.74 kg m^{-3} *[1 mark]*
  density of radon = 9.73 kg m^{-3} *[1 mark]*

The densities of the noble gases increase down the group.

Section 15 — Rates of Reaction and Energy Changes

Page 119 — Reaction Rates

1   If the rate is higher than the rate of the original reaction, the gas will be produced **more quickly** *[1 mark]*.
If the rate is lower than the rate of the original reaction, the gas will be produced **more slowly** *[1 mark]*.

2 a)   Watch the black mark through the solution and stop the stopwatch when it disappears *[1 mark]*.

b)   It shows when the solution has gone cloudy *[1 mark]*.

c)   E.g. the results are subjective / different people might not agree exactly when the black mark disappears *[1 mark]*.

Page 120 — Rate Experiments Involving Gases

1   B *[1 mark]*

2 a)   Concentration: A *[1 mark]*
Reason: e.g. the reaction finished sooner *[1 mark]*.

b)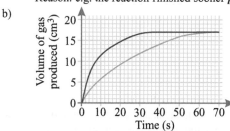

[1 mark for your curve having a steeper gradient at the start. 1 mark for your curve finishing at the same volume of gas as the original curve]

Pages 121-122 — Calculating Rates

1 a) $4.0 \div 125 = $ **0.032** units *[2 marks for correct answer, otherwise 1 mark for correct working]*

b)   B *[1 mark]*

2 a)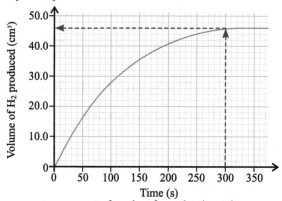

mean rate = amount of product formed ÷ time taken
$= 46.0 \div 300 = 0.1533... = $ **0.153 cm³ s⁻¹**
[2 marks for correct answer, otherwise 1 mark for correct working]

You can work out from a graph when a reaction has finished by finding the point where the line goes flat.

b)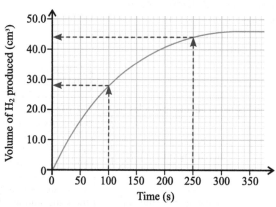

volume of H_2 produced $= 44.0 - 28.0 = 16$ cm³
time difference $= 250 - 100 = 150$ s
mean rate = amount of product formed ÷ time taken
$= 16.0 \div 150 = 0.10666... = $ **0.107 cm³ s⁻¹**
[4 marks for correct answer, otherwise 1 mark for working out the volume of H_2 produced, 1 mark for calculating the time difference and 1 mark for correct working when calculating the mean rate]

3 a)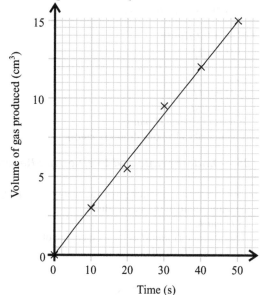

[2 marks — 1 marks for all points plotted correctly, 1 mark for line of best fit]

b)   change in $y = 12 - 3 = 9$
change in $x = 40 - 10 = 30$
gradient = change in y ÷ change in x = **0.3**
[2 marks for correct answer, otherwise 1 mark for correct working]

You can choose any points on the graph to work out the change in y and change in x — they will all give the same gradient.

c)   0.3 cm³ s⁻¹ *[1 mark]*

20

Page 123 — Collision Theory

Warm-up

You should have circled the reaction that uses the lump of calcium carbonate.

1

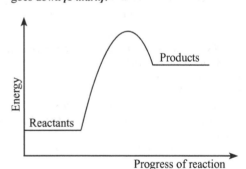

[3 marks — 1 mark for each correct line]

2 a) Increasing the concentration of acid increases the number of acid particles in the same volume *[1 mark]*. This means the acid particles are more likely to collide with zinc particles *[1 mark]*.

   b) activation energy *[1 mark]*

Page 124 — Catalysts

1   D *[1 mark]*

Catalysts decrease the activation energy needed for a reaction by providing a different reaction pathway.

2 a) i) A *[1 mark]*
     ii) C *[1 mark]*
   b) It doesn't change *[1 mark]*.
   c) E.g. to make alcoholic drinks *[1 mark]*.

Page 125 — Endothermic and Exothermic Reactions

Warm-up

An exothermic reaction is one that **gives out** energy. This is shown by a **rise** in the temperature of the surroundings.

1   B *[1 mark]*

2 a) Endothermic *[1 mark]* as the temperature of the surroundings goes down *[1 mark]*.

   b)

[1 mark for reactants and products correctly labelled and at appropriate energies, 1 mark for correct shape of curve]

Page 126 — Bond Energies and Activation Energy

1   C *[1 mark]*

2 a) exothermic *[1 mark]*
   b) i)

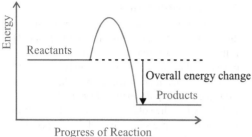

   [1 mark]
     ii)

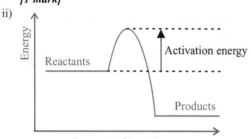

   [1 mark]

   c) E.g. activation energy is the smallest amount of energy needed for bonds to break and a reaction to start / activation energy is the minimum amount of energy needed for a reaction to take place *[1 mark]*.

Page 127 — Measuring Temperature Changes

1 a) Change: e.g. put the polystyrene cup in a beaker filled with cotton wool / add a lid to the polystyrene cup *[1 mark]*. Reason: e.g. to reduce the amount of energy lost to the surroundings *[1 mark]*.

   b) 4, 2, 1, 3 *[2 marks for all four correct, otherwise 1 mark for 2 correct answers]*

   c) 31 – 18 = **13 °C** *[1 mark]*

   d) Independent: concentration of acid *[1 mark]*
      Dependent: temperature change *[1 mark]*

Section 16 — Fuels and Earth Science

Page 128 — Fractional Distillation

Warm-up

Bitumen — Surfacing roads and roofs.

Diesel — Fuel for cars, lorries and trains.

Kerosene — Fuel for aircraft.

1 a) A *[1 mark]*
   b) D *[1 mark]*
   c) B *[1 mark]*

2 a) alkanes *[1 mark]*
   b) One day it will run out / it is being used at a much faster rate than the rate at which it is being reformed *[1 mark]*.

Page 129 — Hydrocarbons

1 a) A compound formed from hydrogen and carbon *[1 mark]* only *[1 mark]*.
   b) CH_2 *[1 mark]*
   c) Increasing chain length increases their viscosity *[1 mark]*.

2 a) Hydrocarbon A: it does not ignite/is hard to ignite *[1 mark]*
      Hydrocarbon B: it ignites/is easy to ignite *[1 mark]*
   b) Hydrocarbon A will have a higher boiling point because more energy is needed the break the forces between big molecules so they have higher boiling points *[1 mark]*.

Page 130 — Combustion of Fuels

1 a) Any one from: petrol/kerosene/diesel oil *[1 mark]*
  b) energy is given out / exothermic *[1 mark]*
  c) Complete combustion: hydrocarbon + oxygen → **carbon dioxide + water** *[1 mark]*
  d) Incomplete combustion happens if there's not enough oxygen for complete combustion *[1 mark]*.
  e) CO/carbon monoxide and C/carbon/soot *[1 mark]*
2 a) E.g. they can cause breathing problems *[1 mark]*.
  b) Name: carbon monoxide *[1 mark]*
    Explanation: carbon monoxide binds to red blood cells *[1 mark]*. This stops them carrying oxygen around the body / means they carry less oxygen around the body *[1 mark]*.

Page 131 — Pollutants

1 Sulfur dioxide — combustion of fossil fuels that contain sulfur impurities.
  Nitrogen oxides — reaction of gases in the air caused by the heat of burning fossil fuels.
  [1 mark for each correct answer]
2 a) e.g. sulfur dioxide / nitrogen oxides *[1 mark]*
  b) Any two from: e.g. damage to plants / buildings / statues / metals *[2 marks — 1 mark for each correct answer]*.
3 a) E.g. nitrogen oxides cause respiratory problems *[1 mark]* and contribute to acid rain *[1 mark]*.
  b) i) Any two from: e.g. less polluting than burning hydrocarbons / hydrogen fuel comes from a reaction with water, which is renewable / the water that's produced in the reaction in the vehicle can be used to make more hydrogen *[2 marks — 1 mark for each correct answer]*.
    ii) Any two from: e.g. expensive/specialised equipment is required / making the hydrogen is expensive / making the gas uses energy which has likely come from fossil fuels / hydrogen is hard to store / hydrogen fuel is not widely available so it is difficult to refuel easily *[2 marks — 1 mark for each correct answer]*.

Pages 132-133 — Cracking

1 a) The breaking down of long saturated (alkane) molecules into smaller unsaturated (alkene) and alkane molecules *[1 mark]*.
  b) alkanes *[1 mark]*, alkenes *[1 mark]*
  c) E.g. shorter chain hydrocarbons are more useful/can be used for more applications than long chain hydrocarbons *[1 mark]*.
2 From top to bottom of the table: false, true, true, true *[4 marks —1 mark of each correct answer]*
3 a) The hydrocarbon vapour is flammable *[1 mark]*.
    The bung prevents the vapour from escaping the boiling tube and igniting *[1 mark]*.
  b) The student could estimate the volume of gas produced by the reaction by observing how much water is pushed out of a test tube with a known volume *[1 mark]*.
  c) A measuring cylinder has a scale which could be used to more accurately measure the volume of gas *[1 mark]*.
  d) The cold water could cause the boiling tube to crack *[1 mark]*.
  e) E.g. the temperature of the reaction *[1 mark]*.

Page 134 — The Atmosphere

Warm-up
Oxygen levels began to rise — 4
The early atmosphere formed — 1
The oceans formed — 2
Plants evolved — 3
1 a) From plants photosynthesising *[1 mark]*.
  b) If a gas is oxygen, it will relight a glowing splint *[1 mark]*.
  c) It condensed to form the oceans *[1 mark]*.
2 How to grade your answer:
  Level 0: There is no relevant information. *[No marks]*
  Level 1: There is a brief description of how carbon dioxide was originally released into the atmosphere and one point briefly describing how it was later removed. The points made are basic and not linked together *[1 to 2 marks]*.
  Level 2: There is some description of how carbon dioxide was originally released into the atmosphere and at least two points describing how it was later removed. There is some reference to the data in Figure 1. Some of the points made are linked together *[3 to 4 marks]*.
  Level 3: There is a good description of how carbon dioxide was originally released into the atmosphere and detailed points describing how it was later removed. There is a clear explanation of how the data in Figure 1 supports this theory. The points made are well-linked and the answer has a clear and logical structure *[5 to 6 marks]*.
  Here are some points your answer may include:
  In the first billion years of Earth, carbon dioxide was released by erupting volcanoes that covered the Earth's surface.
  The early atmosphere contained mostly carbon dioxide.
  Over time, carbon dioxide was removed from the atmosphere.
  Much of the carbon dioxide dissolved in the oceans.
  Green plants took in carbon dioxide through photosynthesis.
  The data in Figure 1 suggests that organisms living longer ago were able to survive in high levels of carbon dioxide.
  Organisms living more recently couldn't survive in high levels of carbon dioxide.
  This supports the conclusion that carbon dioxide levels have decreased since the atmosphere was formed.

Pages 135-137 — Climate Change And The Greenhouse Effect

1 a) Change: it increases it *[1 mark]*.
    Example: Any one from: e.g. more people means that more energy is needed for heating/transport/lighting *[1 mark]*.
  b) From top to bottom of the table: government, government, small business, small business *[4 marks — 1 mark for each correct answer]*
2 a) increasing *[1 mark]*
  b) E.g. changing rainfall patterns *[1 mark]* and severe flooding due to melting polar ice caps *[1 mark]*.
  c) E.g. increased levels of greenhouse gases in the atmosphere *[1 mark]*.
3 a) Any two from: water vapour, methane, carbon dioxide *[1 mark]*
  b) The sun gives out **radiation** *[1 mark]*.
    The Earth reflects this as **thermal** *[1 mark]* radiation.
    This radiation is **absorbed** *[1 mark]* by greenhouse gases and then given out in all directions.
    Some heads back to Earth and **warms** *[1 mark]* the Earth's surface.

4 a) They have increased *[1 mark]*.

b) Any one from: e.g. burning fossil fuels / increasing population means more energy is needed for cooking/ transport/heating/lighting *[1 mark]*.

c) Any two from: e.g. there are no records past a certain point / data was taken at fewer locations / indirect data (e.g. tree rings) is less precise than current measurements / some measurements only show what the conditions were like at one location *[2 marks — 1 mark for each correct answer]*.

5 a) As carbon dioxide levels increased, the global temperature also increased *[1 mark]*.

b) E.g. the table doesn't include data from before 1960 *[1 mark]* so you cannot tell from the table what was happening to CO_2 levels before that date *[1 mark]*. / The table doesn't include data in the years between the ones given *[1 mark]* so you cannot tell from the table what was happening to CO_2 levels in the years in between *[1 mark]*.

c) Higher temperatures may cause ice caps to melt *[1 mark]*, reducing the amount of ice available for scientists to collect *[1 mark]*.

Section 17 — Motion and Forces

Page 138 — Distance, Displacement, Speed and Velocity

1 Scalar and vector quantities both have a magnitude/size *[1 mark]*, but vectors have a direction while scalars do not *[1 mark]*.

2 a) 7 m *[1 mark]*

b) 12 m *[1 mark]*

c) 2 m *[1 mark]*

As the scale is 1 cm = 1 m the number of metres measured is equal to the number of centimetres measured.

3 Rearrange the equation for time:
time = distance ÷ average speed
typical walking speed = 1.4 m/s (accept 1–2 m/s)
distance travelled = 7 km = 7000 m
so time = 7000 ÷ 1.4
   = 5000 s (accept 3500–7000 s)
[4 marks for correct answer, otherwise 1 mark for correctly rearranging the equation, 1 mark for sensible value of typical walking speed and 1 mark for correct conversion and substitution]

Page 139 — Acceleration

Warm-up
A sprinter starting a race — 1.5 m/s²
A falling object — 10 m/s²
A bullet shot from a gun — 2×10^5 m/s²

1 acceleration = change in velocity ÷ time taken
Read a pair of values from the table
e.g. acceleration = 4 ÷ 1
   = 4 m/s²
[3 marks for correct answer, otherwise 1 mark for correctly reading from the table and 1 mark for correct substitution]
You'd still get all the marks here if you correctly calculated the acceleration using the time and velocity values from the third or fourth column in the table instead.

2 Car C *[1 mark]* because all the cars' speeds decrease by the same amount (10 m/s) and car C's speed changes in the shortest time *[1 mark]*.

3 $v^2 - u^2 = 2 \times a \times x$
Rearrange for acceleration:
$a = (v^2 - u^2) \div (2 \times x)$
   $= (32^2 - 18^2) \div (2 \times 350)$
   = 1.0 m/s²
[3 marks for correct answer, otherwise 1 mark for correct rearrangement and 1 mark for correct substitution]

Page 140 — Distance/Time Graphs

1 a)
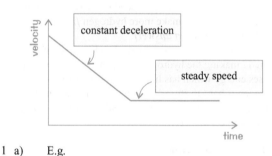

[1 mark for all points plotted correctly, 1 mark for straight line connecting all points]

b) 355 m (accept 350–360 m) *[1 mark]*

c) 215 s (accept 210–220 s) *[1 mark]*

d) The boat's speed stays constant *[1 mark]*.

Page 141 — Velocity/Time Graphs

Warm-up

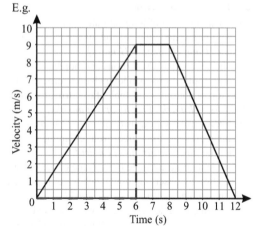

1 a) E.g.

$a = \Delta v \div t$ or gradient of line
acceleration = $(9 - 0) \div (6 - 0)$
   = 1.5 m/s²
[3 marks for correct answer, otherwise 1 mark for correctly reading a pair of v and t values from the graph and 1 mark for a correct method of calculation of the gradient]

b) Distance travelled is given by the area beneath the graph between 6 s and 8 s.
area of a rectangle = width × height
width = 8 − 6 = 2, height = 9
distance travelled = 2 × 9 = **18 m**
[3 marks for correct answer, otherwise 1 mark for correctly identifying the region of constant speed on graph and 1 mark for a correct method of area calculation]

Pages 142-143 — Weight

Warm-up

1) True, 2) False, 3) False

1   B *[1 mark]*

2 a)   weight = mass × gravitational field strength *[1 mark]*

  b)   weight = 185 × 10

              = **1850 N**

      [2 marks for correct answer, otherwise 1 mark for correct substitution.]

  c)   Rearrange the weight equation for gravitational field strength:

      gravitational field strength = weight ÷ mass

                             = 703 ÷ 185

                             = **3.8 N/kg**

      [3 marks for correct answer, otherwise 1 mark for correct rearrangement and 1 mark for correct substitution]

3 a)   E.g. place each disc on a mass balance, and record the mass displayed *[1 mark]*.

  b)   systematic error *[1 mark]*

A systematic error is where all your results are off by the same amount. In this example, each measurement of the weight is too large, because the same weight of the tray has been included in every measurement.

  c) i) E.g.

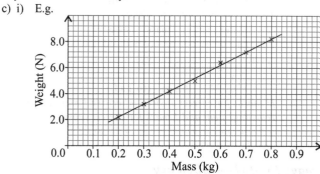

      [1 mark for points for 0.3 kg and 0.6 kg plotted correctly. 1 mark for a straight line of best fit drawn through or close to all points]

    ii) E.g. $g = \text{gradient} = \dfrac{\text{change in } y}{\text{change in } x} = \dfrac{8.4 - 2.0}{0.82 - 0.18}$ *[1 mark]*

                       = **10 N/kg** *[1 mark]*

You'll get the calculation marks here as long as your calculation of the gradient is correct for your line of best fit.

Page 144 — Resultant Force and Newton's First Law

1   C *[1 mark]*

The resultant force is non-zero for runner C, as the two forces acting on him are different sizes.

2   Newton's First Law states that if the **resultant** force acting on a moving object is zero, the velocity of the object will **stay the same**.

      If the force is non-zero and acts in the opposite direction to the movement of the object, the velocity of the object will **decrease**. *[3 marks — 1 mark for each correct answer]*

3 a)   The resultant force on the van is zero *[1 mark]* because according to Newton's First Law, an object must experience a zero resultant force to remain at rest *[1 mark]*.

  b)   There is a resultant force in the direction of the van's motion/ up the hill as the van accelerates *[1 mark]*. When the van travels at a constant speed, the resultant force on it is zero *[1 mark]*.

Page 145 — Newton's Second Law

1 a)   force = mass × acceleration *[1 mark]*

  b)   Rearrange the equation for acceleration:

      acceleration = force ÷ mass

      acceleration = 2400 ÷ 400 = **6 m/s²**

      [3 marks for correct answer, otherwise 1 mark for correct rearrangement and 1 mark for correct substitution]

2   How to grade your answer:

      Level 0:   There is no relevant information. *[No marks]*

      Level 1:   There is a description of the dangers of applying a large braking force while at a high speed. There is no attempt to link this to Newton's Second Law. *[1 to 2 marks]*

      Level 2:   There is a brief explanation of how applying a large braking force while at a high speed can be dangerous. The explanation is linked to Newton's Second Law. *[3 to 4 marks]*

      Level 3:   There is a clear and detailed explanation of how applying a large braking force while at a high speed can be dangerous. The explanation is linked to Newton's Second Law. *[5 to 6 marks]*

      Here are some points your answer may include:

      If a driver applies a large braking fore while at a high speed, their vehicle will experience a large change in speed.

      The change in speed will occur over a short period of time.

      This means the vehicle will experience a large deceleration (since acceleration = change in velocity ÷ time taken).

      A large deceleration will cause a large force to act on the vehicle and its driver (since force = mass × acceleration).

      The large forces acting on the driver can harm them.

      Large forces can also cause the brakes to overheat.

      This can damage the brakes and stop them working as well, which could cause a collision, as the vehicle may not stop soon enough.

      A large braking force can also cause the car to skid.

      This could cause the vehicle to not stop in time, and cause a collision.

Page 146 — Investigating Motion

1 a)   Each light gate records the speed of the trolley as it passes through the gate *[1 mark]*. They also record how long it takes the trolley to travel between the gates *[1 mark]*. You (or some computer software) can then use these values to calculate the acceleration of the trolley, using acceleration = change in speed ÷ time *[1 mark]*.

  b)   E.g. as force increases, the acceleration of the trolley increases *[1 mark]*.

  c)   E.g. at a force of 2.0 N, the acceleration is 1.0 m/s²

      So mass = force ÷ acceleration

                   = 2.0 ÷ 1.0

                   = **2.0 kg**

      [3 marks for correct answer, otherwise 1 mark for correct rearrangement and 1 mark for correctly reading force and acceleration from the graph and substituting them into the equation]

You'll still get the marks if you took readings from a different part of the graph, so long as you get the correct final answer.

  d)   The acceleration will be smaller *[1 mark]*.

Page 147 — Newton's Third Law

Warm-up

When two objects interact, they exert equal and opposite forces on each other.

1   D *[1 mark]*

2 a)   There is no resultant force acting on the object / the resultant force acting on the object is zero *[1 mark]*.

  b)   640 N *[1 mark]*

Page 148 — Stopping Distances

1   A *[1 mark]*

2 a)   E.g. the distance travelled during the driver's reaction time *[1 mark]*

  b)   Drinking alcohol would increase his thinking distance *[1 mark]*, because it will increase his reaction time *[1 mark]*.

  c)   E.g. speed of the car / drug use / tiredness *[1 mark]*.

3 a)   E.g. the distance travelled under the braking force of the vehicle *[1 mark]*.

  b)   The car's braking distance will increase *[1 mark]* because the ice will reduce the grip between the tyres and the road, and may cause the car to skid *[1 mark]*.

Page 149 — Reaction Times

1 a)   E.g. reaction times are too short to be measured accurately by a stopwatch *[1 mark]*.

  b)   Student C's reaction time is fastest *[1 mark]* because the ruler fell the shortest distance (on average) before they caught it *[1 mark]*.

  c)   Any two from: e.g. use the same ruler / always have the same person dropping the ruler / test the students at the same time of day / remove distractions for all students.
[2 marks — 1 mark for each correct answer]

  d)   Their reaction times are likely to be longer than usual *[1 mark]*.

  e)   Student D's calculation must be wrong because his calculated reaction time is much larger than typical reaction times of 0.2 - 0.9s *[1 mark]*.

Section 18 — Conservation of Energy

Page 150 — Energy Stores and Conservation of Energy

1   D *[1 mark]*

2   A car slowing down without braking. — kinetic energy store
A mug of hot tea cooling down. — thermal energy store
A stretched spring returning to its original shape. — elastic potential energy store
A battery in a circuit. — chemical energy store
[3 marks for all four correct, otherwise 2 marks for three correct and 1 mark for one or two correct]

3 a)   E.g. in a closed system, no energy can be transferred into or out of the system *[1 mark]*.

  b)   E.g. energy is transferred from the thermal energy store of the spoon (by heating) *[1 mark]* to the thermal energy store of the water *[1 mark]*.

Page 151 — Energy Transfers

Warm-up
mechanically

1   An electric kettle is used to heat some water. When the kettle is on, energy is transferred **electrically** to the thermal energy store of the kettle's heating element. The energy is then transferred to the water **by heating**. The energy is transferred to the water's **thermal** energy store.
[3 marks —1 mark for each correct answer]

2 a)   Energy is transferred mechanically *[1 mark]* from the gravitational potential energy store of the sledge *[1 mark]* to the kinetic energy store of the sledge *[1 mark]*.

  b)   Energy is transferred mechanically *[1 mark]* from the kinetic energy store of the sledge *[1 mark]* to the thermal energy stores of the ground and the sledge *[1 mark]*.

Page 152 — Kinetic and Potential Energy Stores

1   Convert from kJ to J:
kinetic energy = $1.1 \times 1000 = 1100$ J
kinetic energy = $0.5 \times$ mass $\times$ (speed)^2
Rearrange the equation for mass:
mass = $(2 \times$ kinetic energy$) \div$ (speed)^2
mass = $(2 \times 1100) \div (5.0)^2$
     = **88 kg**
[3 marks for correct answer, otherwise 1 mark for correct rearrangement and 1 mark for correct conversion and substitution]

2 a)   change in gravitational potential energy = mass $\times$ gravitational field strength $\times$ change in vertical height *[1 mark]*

  b)   change in gravitational potential energy = $0.50 \times 10 \times 2.0$
     = **10 J**
[2 marks for correct answer, otherwise 1 mark for correct substitution]

  c)   kinetic energy = ½ $\times$ mass $\times$ (speed)^2
To rearrange the kinetic energy equation for speed, multiply both sides by 2:
$2 \times$ kinetic energy = mass $\times$ (speed)^2
Then divide both sides by mass:
$(2 \times$ kinetic energy$) \div$ mass = (speed)^2
Then take the square root of both sides to get:
speed = $\sqrt{(2 \times \text{kinetic energy}) \div \text{mass}}$
     = $\sqrt{(2 \times 10) \div 0.50}$
     = 6.324... = **6.3 m/s (to 2 s.f.)**
[3 marks for correct answer, otherwise 1 mark for correct rearrangement and 1 mark for correct substitution]

If you got a different answer in part a), you would still get the marks here if you used your answer and the correct method.

Pages 153-154 — Efficiency

1 a)   Fan A *[1 mark]*, because it transfers more energy usefully than fans B or C and they are all supplied with the same amount of energy *[1 mark]*.

  b)   Energy is transferred mechanically (because of work done against friction) *[1 mark]* from the kinetic energy store of the fan's parts *[1 mark]* to their thermal energy stores *[1 mark]*.

2 a)   efficiency = $\dfrac{\text{useful energy transferred by the device}}{\text{total energy supplied to the device}}$ *[1 mark]*

  b)   efficiency = $72\% = 0.72$
rearrange the efficiency equation for total energy supplied:
total energy supplied to the device
     = useful energy transferred by the device $\div$ efficiency
     = $18\,000 \div 0.72$
     = **25 000 J**
[3 marks for correct answer, otherwise 1 mark for correct rearrangement and 1 mark for correct conversion and substitution]

3 a)   E.g. getting an electric shock from the use of electricity *[1 mark]*, and getting burnt by the hot water *[1 mark]*.

  b)   B *[1 mark]*

  c)   E.g. the graph in Figure 2 shows that efficiency increases as the mass of water increases *[1 mark]*.

Page 155 — Reducing Unwanted Energy Transfers

1   He could lubricate the bike chain/gears *[1 mark]*. This would reduce the friction between the chain and the gears *[1 mark]*.

2 a)   D *[1 mark]*
Bricks that are thicker and have a lower thermal conductivity will transfer energy through them more slowly. This will reduce the rate of cooling of the house.

   b)   Thickness of useful energy arrow = 3 squares
        So, 1 square = 27 ÷ 3 = 9 kJ
        Thickness of left hand side of the diagram = 5 squares
        So, energy supplied = 5 × 9 = **45 kJ**
        [3 marks for correct answer, otherwise 1 mark for finding the energy represented by 1 square and 1 mark for a correct method of calculation]
In these energy transfer diagrams, the thickness of each part of the diagram tells you how much energy is transferred. You would also have gotten the marks if you found the thickness of the useful and wasted arrows and added them together.

Page 156 — Energy Resources

Warm-up
Renewable — bio-fuel, solar, tidal, hydro-electricity, wind
Non-renewable — oil, coal, natural gas, nuclear fuel

1 a)   coal, oil, (natural) gas
        [3 marks — 1 mark for each correct answer]
   b)   E.g. generating electricity / heating *[1 mark]*
   c)   C *[1 mark]*

2   E.g. non-renewable energy resources will run out one day *[1 mark]* but renewable energy resources will never run out *[1 mark]*.

Page 157 — More Energy Resources

1 a)   C *[1 mark]*
   b)   E.g. hydro-electric power plants can increase electricity generation when there's extra demand (but tidal barrages cannot) *[1 mark]*.

2   E.g. the average wind speed between October and March was higher than the average wind speed between April and September, so wind turbines will be able to generate more electricity between October and March *[1 mark]*. Between April and September, the average number of daylight hours was higher than the average number of daylight hours between October and March, so solar panels will be able to generate more electricity between April and September *[1 mark]*. So when one of the methods of generating electricity is producing less electricity, the other method will be producing more *[1 mark]*. By installing both, the university will have a more constant and reliable electricity supply throughout the year *[1 mark]*.

Page 158 — Trends in Energy Resource Use

1 a)   56 + 10 + 16 = **82 %**
        [2 marks for correct answer, otherwise 1 mark for reading all three values correctly from the graph]
   b)   E.g. the country is using a larger percentage of renewable energy resources to generate electricity in 2015 than 1995 / overall, they are using a smaller percentage of fossil fuels to generate their electricity in 2015 than they were in 1995 / the percentage of electricity generated from nuclear power is lower in 1995 compared to 2015 *[1 mark]*.

2 a)   E.g. we now know that burning fossil fuels is bad for the environment *[1 mark]*, so more people want to use renewable energy resources that damage the environment less *[1 mark]*. / Fossil fuel reserves will run out *[1 mark]*, so we have to find an alternative for them *[1 mark]*. / Pressure from the public and other countries has led to government targets for the use of renewable energy resources *[1 mark]*, which puts pressure on energy providers to build power plants that use renewable energy resources *[1 mark]*.

   b)   How to grade your answer:
        Level 0:   There is no relevant information. *[No marks]*
        Level 1:   At least two factors that limit the increase in use of renewable energy resources. A brief explanation for one of the factors is given. *[1 to 2 marks]*
        Level 2:   There is a clear explanation of at least two factors that limit the increase in use of renewable energy resources. *[3 to 4 marks]*
        Level 3:   There is a clear and detailed explanation of at least three factors that limit the increase in use of renewable energy resources. *[5 to 6 marks]*

Here are some points your answer may include:
Building new power plants to replace existing fossil fuel powered ones is expensive.
Some renewable energy resources are less reliable than fossil fuels. So a mixture of different energy resources would need to be used, which is also more expensive than just using fossil fuels.
Research into improving renewable energy resources costs money and will take time.
Energy companies are unlikely to pay for all these costs, so this extra cost needs to be paid through energy bills or taxes.
Governments may not want to raise taxes as it may make them unpopular with the public.
Some people don't want to or can't afford to pay the extra cost.
Personal products that use renewable energy resources, like hybrid cars, are generally more expensive than similar ones that use fossil fuels.

Section 19 — Waves and the Electromagnetic Spectrum

Page 159 — Wave Basics

Warm-up
sound waves — L
water waves — T
electromagnetic waves — T

1 a)
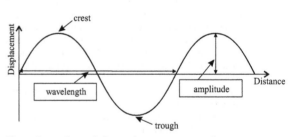
        [2 marks — 1 mark for each correct answer]
   b)   The number of complete waves which pass a point in one second *[1 mark]*.
   c)   The vibrations in longitudinal waves are in the same direction as the direction the wave is travelling in *[1 mark]*. But in transverse waves, the vibration is perpendicular (at right angles) to the direction the wave is travelling in *[1 mark]*.

2   She's incorrect. It is the wave, not the water, that moves across the puddle so the leaf will just move up and down *[1 mark]*.

Page 160 — Wave Speed

1   Convert distance to m:
        114 cm = 114 ÷ 100 = 1.14 m
        wave speed = distance ÷ time, so
        time = distance ÷ wave speed
        time = 1.14 ÷ 0.19
              = **6.0 s**
        [3 marks for correct answer, otherwise 1 mark for correct rearrangement and 1 mark for correct conversion and substitution]

2 a)   Correct order = D, E, B, A, C
        [3 marks for all in correct order, otherwise 2 marks for three in correct order (not including D), or 1 mark for two in correct order (not including D)]
    b)   wave speed = frequency × wavelength *[1 mark]*
    c)   wave speed = 50.0 × 6.80 = **340 m/s**
        [2 marks for correct answer, otherwise 1 mark for correct substitution]

Page 161 — Investigating Waves

1   E.g. use the microphone to measure the frequency of the sound waves produced as the rod is hit *[1 mark]*. The frequency of the loudest sound wave recorded is the same frequency as the peak frequency wave in the rod *[1 mark]*.

2   How to grade your answer:
        Level 0:   There is no relevant information. *[No marks]*
        Level 1:   A simple method to find the speed of waves in the tank is partly outlined. *[1 to 2 marks]*
        Level 2:   A method to find the speed of waves in the tank is outlined in some detail, with reference to finding the wavelength and frequency. *[3 to 4 marks]*
        Level 3:   A method to find the speed of waves in the tank is fully explained in detail, including an explanation of how to find the wavelength and frequency. *[5 to 6 marks]*
        Here are some points your answer may include:
        Use the signal generator to produce waves at a fixed frequency.
        Count the number of waves passing a point in 10 seconds.
        Divide this value by 10 to find the frequency of the waves.
        The strobe light casts shadows on the sheet of paper below the tank.
        Change the frequency of the strobe light until the shadows appear to stop moving.
        This happens when the frequency of the strobe light is the same frequency as the waves.
        Now the shadows appear still, measure the across 10 gaps between the shadow lines using a ruler.
        Divide this measurement by 10 to find the wavelength of the waves.
        Multiply the frequency by the wavelength you calculated to find the wave speed (as $v = f\lambda$).

Page 162 — Refraction

1   Refraction is when a wave **changes direction** after it hits a boundary. A wave that is travelling along the normal **will not** refract after it hits the boundary.
        [2 marks — 1 mark for each correct answer]

2   E.g.

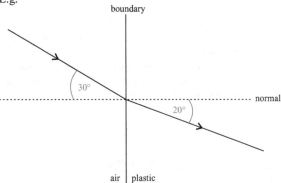

        [1 mark for an incident ray drawn on the left of the boundary and a refracted ray drawn on the right of the boundary with correct arrows on both rays, 1 mark for correctly drawn normal, 1 mark for incident ray at 30° to the normal (on either side of the normal), 1 mark for refracted ray at 20° to the normal on the opposite side of the normal to the incident ray]
You don't need to have labelled the angles in your diagram, we've just included them here to make it clearer.

3   It will be larger than 20° *[1 mark]*.
        E.g. when light travelled from air to water, the light ray bent towards the normal/the angle of refraction was smaller than the angle of incidence. This means that for a light ray travelling from water to air, the ray will bend away from the normal/the angle of refraction will be larger than the angle of incidence *[1 mark]*. / As the light ray will be travelling from a denser to a less dense material, it must bend away from the normal *[1 mark]*

Page 163 — Investigating Refraction

1 a)   E.g. a ray box creates a thin ray of light which lets you make more accurate measurements of angles *[1 mark]*
    b)

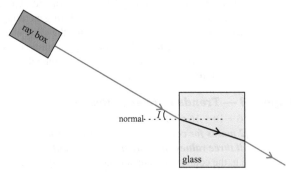

        [1 mark for correctly completed diagram]
    c)   30° (Allow any answer between 29° and 31°) *[1 mark]*
    d)   Any two from: e.g. use the same glass block / make sure the pencil is always sharp / use the same protractor / use the same ray box / use the same ruler.
        [2 marks — 1 mark for each correct answer]

Page 164 — Electromagnetic Waves

1 a) In this order: Microwaves *[1 mark]*, X-rays *[1 mark]*.
  b) Arrow must point to the left (i.e. from gamma rays to radio waves) *[1 mark]*.
  c) All waves in the electromagnetic spectrum are **transverse** waves. All electromagnetic waves travel at the same speed in **a vacuum**.
    [2 marks — 1 mark for each correct answer]
2 a) The higher the frequency, the more harmful the electromagnetic wave can be *[1 mark]*.
  b) Ultraviolet waves *[1 mark]*.
  c) Microwaves can be absorbed by the body *[1 mark]*. This can cause cells inside your body to heat up, which can damage them *[1 mark]*.
  d) Gamma rays can kill cells in the body *[1 mark]* or cause mutations in cells which can cause cancer *[1 mark]*.

Page 165 — Uses of EM Waves

Warm-up
True, False, True
1 a) When food is cooked in a microwave oven, water in the food **absorbs** microwaves. This causes the temperature of the food to **increase**. *[2 marks — 1 mark for each correct answer]*
  b) Any one from: e.g. satellite transmissions / communication with satellites *[1 mark]*
2 a) A *[1 mark]*
  b) E.g. it detects infrared radiation emitted by an object and converts this into an image on a screen *[1 mark]*. Objects at different temperatures give out different amounts of infrared radiation, so they appear brighter/as different colours *[1 mark]*.

Page 166 — More Uses of EM Waves

1 A *[1 mark]*
2 a) If ultraviolet light is shone on the wallet, the security pen ink will glow/emit visible light *[1 mark]*.
  b) Any one from: e.g. detecting forged bank notes/passports *[1 mark]*
3 a) E.g. to treat cancer / to sterilise medical instruments/equipment *[2 marks — 1 mark for each correct]*
  b) X-rays *[1 mark]*. E.g. X-ray images are used to check for broken bones *[1 mark]*.

Section 20 — Radioactivity

Page 167 — The Atomic Model

Warm-up
$1 \times 10\text{–}10$ m
1 a) Protons have a relative charge of +1 and neutrons have a relative charge of 0. Electrons have a relative charge of –1. An atom has an overall charge of 0.
    [4 marks — 1 mark for each correct answer]
  b) Neutron: 1
    Electron: 0.0005
    [2 marks — 1 mark for each correct answer]
2 a) The protons and neutrons make up a central nucleus *[1 mark]* and the electrons orbit/surround the nucleus *[1 mark]*.
  b) The nucleus is made up of protons and neutrons, which have much larger relative masses than electrons *[1 mark]*. So almost all of the mass is in the centre/nucleus *[1 mark]*.

Page 168 — More on the Atomic Model

1 a) C *[1 mark]*
  b) +1 *[1 mark]*
2 a) E.g. the electron has absorbed electromagnetic radiation *[1 mark]*.
  b) The electron moves (into a lower energy level) closer to the nucleus [1 mark].
3 a) The plum pudding model *[1 mark]*. In this model, atoms were thought of as spheres of positive charge, with electrons stuck in them *[1 mark]*.
  b) Most of the particles went straight through the foil [1 mark]. This led Rutherford to believe that most of the atom was empty space *[1 mark]*.
    Some alpha particles changed direction or 'bounced back' *[1 mark]*.
    This led Rutherford to believe that the nucleus was positively-charged, as it repelled the positively-charged alpha particles *[1 mark]*.

Page 169-170 — Isotopes and Nuclear Radiation

Warm-up
A — mass number, Z — atomic number, X — element symbol
1 a) Gamma rays — Electromagnetic radiation from the nucleus.
    Isotopes — Atoms whose nuclei have the same positive charge but different nuclear masses.
    Alpha particles — Particles that are the same as helium nuclei.
    [2 marks for all 3 correct lines drawn, otherwise 1 mark for one correct line drawn]
  b) beta-minus decay *[1 mark]*
2 E.g. alpha particles can't pass through paper *[1 mark]*. Gamma rays can pass through paper easily, so the radiation measured would not change much with the thickness of the paper *[1 mark]*.
3 a) i) The (use of) lead blocks *[1 mark]*.
    ii) They will absorb radiation emitted from the beta source, preventing it from reaching, and potentially harming, the engineer *[1 mark]*.
  b) i) The mean is given by the sum of all the values, divided by the number of values, so:
    mean = $(101 + 122 + 105) \div 3$ *[1 mark]*
    = 109.33... = **109 (to nearest whole number)** *[1 mark]*
    ii) uncertainty = range $\div$ 2 = $(122 - 101) \div 2$ *[1 mark]*
    = **10.5** *[1 mark]*

Page 171 — Nuclear Equations

1 a) Mass number: Doesn't change *[1 mark]*.
    Atomic number: Increases by 1 *[1 mark]*.
  b) The charge increases *[1 mark]* because the nucleus now has an extra proton (as a neutron has turned into a proton and an electron) *[1 mark]*.
2 A proton *[1 mark]* changes into a neutron and a positron *[1 mark]*.
3 a) i) $^{1}_{0}$n / neutron *[1 mark]*
    ii) $a = 24 - 1 = 23$ *[1 mark]*
    $b = 7 - 0 = 7$ *[1 mark]*
  b) $^{218}_{84}\text{Po} \rightarrow {}^{214}_{82}\text{Pb} + {}^{4}_{2}\alpha$
    [1 mark for correct mass numbers, 1 mark for correct atomic numbers, 1 mark for correct symbol for alpha particle]

Page 172 — Background Radiation and Activity

1 a)   C *[1 mark]*
  b)   The activity of a source always decreases over time *[1 mark]*.
2 a)   Low-level radiation that is always around us *[1 mark]*.
  b)   Any two from: e.g. rocks / food / air / radiation from space/
       cosmic rays / human activities / nuclear explosions / nuclear
       waste. *[2 marks — 1 mark for each correct answer]*
  c)   E.g. record the count-rate without the source present to find
       the count-rate of the background radiation *[1 mark]*. Record
       the count-rate near to the source and subtract the background
       count-rate to find the count-rate due to the source *[1 mark]*.
  d)   E.g. photographic film *[1 mark]*

Page 173 — Half-Life

1 a)   The time taken for the activity of the sample to decay by half
       [1 mark].
  b)   Radioactive decay is a **random** process. This means you
       can't predict when a certain nucleus will decay. If you have
       a **large** number of nuclei in a sample, you can use the half-
       life to predict the activity of the sample.
       [3 marks — 1 mark for each correct answer].
2 a)   Half of the initial activity is 60 kBq ÷ 2 = 30 kBq
       Reading the time from the graph at 30 kBq:
       Half-life = **75 s** *[1 mark]*
  b)   150 ÷ 75 = 2
       So 2 half-lives occur in the first 150 seconds.
       1st half-life: 6 500 000 ÷ 2 = 3 250 000 undecayed nuclei
       2nd half-life: 3 250 000 ÷ 2 = 1 625 000 undecayed nuclei
       Number of remaining nuclei = **1 600 000 (to 2 s.f.)**
       *[3 marks for correct answer, otherwise 1 mark for correct
       calculation of the number of half-lives in 150 seconds
       and 1 mark for correct calculation of the number of
       undecayed nuclei after two half-lives]*

Page 174 — Irradiation and Contamination

1   A *[1 mark]*
2 a)   Contamination is when unwanted radioactive particles get
       onto or into an object *[1 mark]*. Irradiation is when an object
       is exposed to radiation *[1 mark]*.
  b)   Any two from: e.g. wearing protective gloves / using tongs /
       wearing a protective suit or mask.
       [2 marks — 1 mark for each correct answer]
3   Contamination *[1 mark]*. Alpha particles cannot pass
       through skin, so the risk from irradiation is lower *[1 mark]*.
       However, they are strongly ionising but don't travel far, so
       they can cause lots of damage to a small area inside the
       clockmaker's body (e.g. if atoms get stuck to his fingers and
       then accidentally eaten) *[1 mark]*.

Section 21 — Forces and Energy

Page 175 — Energy Transfers and Systems

Warm-up
Circled: elastic potential, nuclear, thermal.
1   gravitational potential energy store of the apple *[1 mark]*
       kinetic energy store of the apple *[1 mark]*
2 a)   Energy is spread out and is transferred to less useful energy
       stores *[1 mark]*.
  b)   From top to bottom: true, true, false.
       [3 marks — 1 mark for each correct answer]

Page 176 — Forces and Work Done

1   A *[1 mark]*
2

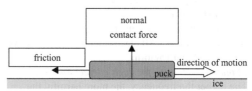

       [2 marks — 1 mark for each correct label]
3 a)   work done = force × distance moved in the direction of the
                    force
                  = 50 × 15
                  = **750 Nm**
       *[2 marks for correct answer, otherwise 1 mark for correct
       substitution]*
  b)   750 J *[1 mark]*

*Remember, work done and energy transferred are the same thing,
and 1 Nm = 1 J.*

Page 177 — Wasted Energy and Power

1 a)   The temperature of the bike chain increases, so energy has
       been transferred to its thermal energy store *[1 mark]*. This
       transfer is not useful, so the energy is wasted *[1 mark]*.
  b)   E.g. lubricate the chain *[1 mark]*.
2 a)   Rearrange the equation for work done:
       work done = power × time taken
                 = 35 × 600
                 = **21 000 J**
       *[3 marks for correct answer, otherwise 1 mark for
       rearranging the equation for work done and 1 mark for
       correct substitution]*
  b)   Energy transferred is the same as work done, so can use the
       given power equation.
       Rearrange the equation for time:
       so time taken = work done ÷ power
                     = 16 800 ÷ 35
                     = **480 s**
       *[3 marks for correct answer, otherwise 1 mark for rearranging
       the equation for time taken and 1 mark for correct substitution]*
3   Convert total energy supplied from kJ to J:
       total energy supplied = 1200 × 1000 = 1 200 000 J
       $\text{efficiency} = \dfrac{\text{useful energy transferred by the device}}{\text{total energy supplied to the device}}$
       Rearrange for useful energy:
       useful energy transferred by the device
         = total energy supplied to the device × efficiency
         = 1 200 000 × 0.7
         = **840 000 J**
       *[3 marks for correct answer, otherwise 1 mark for correct
       rearrangement and 1 mark for correct conversion and
       substitution]*

Section 22 — Electricity and Circuits

Page 178 — Current and Circuits
Warm-up

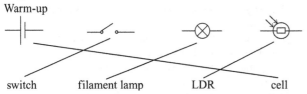

switch   filament lamp   LDR   cell

1   A *[1 mark]*
2 a)   There is no source of potential difference *[1 mark]*.
  b)   electrons *[1 mark]*
3 a)   charge = current × time *[1 mark]*
  b)   Rearrange the equation for current:
     current = charge ÷ time
           = 420 ÷ 120
           = **3.5 A**

[3 marks for correct answer, otherwise 1 mark for correct rearrangement and 1 mark for correct substitution]

Page 179 — Potential Difference and Resistance
Warm-up
True, False, True
1 a)   A *[1 mark]*
  b) $E = Q \times V$
     $E = 150 \times 18 = \mathbf{2700\ J}$

[2 marks for correct answer, otherwise 1 mark for correct substitution]

2 a)   potential difference = current × resistance *[1 mark]*
  b)   resistance = potential difference ÷ current
     resistance = 25 ÷ 3.0
             = 8.333... Ω
             = **8.3 Ω (to 2 s.f.)**

[3 marks for correct answer, otherwise 1 mark for correct rearrangement and 1 mark for correct substitution]

  c)   As the temperature of the resistor increases, the ions in the resistor vibrate more *[1 mark]*. The more the ions vibrate, the harder it is for electrons to pass through the resistor, so the current decreases *[1 mark]*.

Pages 180-181 — I-V Graphs
1 a)   D *[1 mark]*
  b)   In the positive direction, the resistance decreases as current and potential difference increase above a certain amount *[1 mark]*. In the reverse direction, the resistance is very high *[1 mark]*.
2 a)   E.g. set the resistance of the variable resistor *[1 mark]*. Take readings of the current through and the potential difference across the lamp *[1 mark]*. Then change the resistance of the variable resistor by a set amount and take readings of current through and potential difference across the lamp. Repeat these steps to get a range of values of current and p.d. for the lamp *[1 mark]*.
  b)   Read potential difference when current is 2.0 A off the graph.
     potential difference = 6 V
     potential difference = current × resistance
     so, resistance = potential difference ÷ current
                 = 6 ÷ 2.0
                 = **3 Ω**

[4 marks for correct answer, otherwise 1 mark for correct value of potential difference, 1 mark for correct rearrangement and 1 mark for correct substitution]

3 a) i)   E.g.

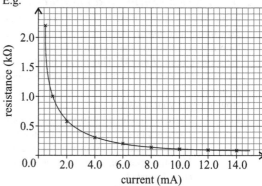

[1 mark for smooth line passing through or close to all points]

    ii)   0.4 kΩ (accept between 0.35 and 0.45 kΩ) *[1 mark]*
Read off the value of resistance for a current of 3.0 mA (halfway between the 2.0 mA and 4.0 mA markers) from your curve of best fit.

  b)   A *[1 mark]*
Diodes have a very high resistance for one direction of current flow but not the opposite, so the student's conclusion is not true for negative values of current.

  c)   Have someone else carry out the same experiment using different equipment *[1 mark]*, and if the results are similar to the student's, then the experiment is reproducible *[1 mark]*.

Page 182 — Circuit Devices
1   C *[1 mark]*
Thermistors have a high resistance at low temperatures. Their resistance decreases as their temperature increases.
2 a)   E.g.

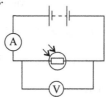

[1 mark for a complete circuit containing an LDR, ammeter and battery in series, 1 mark for showing a voltmeter in parallel across the LDR]

  b)   It decreases *[1 mark]*.

Page 183 — Series and Parallel Circuits
1   It is in series with the filament bulb *[1 mark]*
2 a)   D *[1 mark]*
  b)   Resistor A because it has a larger resistance so it has a larger share of the total p.d. *[1 mark]*
  c)   current = 0.05 A *[1 mark]*
The current is the same everywhere in a series circuit.
  d)   Total potential difference in series circuit = 3 V
     Potential difference across Resistor B in series = 3 − 2
                                     = 1 V
     Potential difference across Resistor B in parallel = 3 V
     Change in potential difference across resistor B = 3 − 1
                                     = **2 V**

[3 marks for correct answer, otherwise 1 mark for correct p.d. across Resistor B in series and 1 mark for correct p.d. across Resistor B in parallel]

When you connect two components in series the total p.d. is shared between all components. When they are in parallel each component has the same p.d. as the supply.

Page 184 — More on Series and Parallel Circuits

1   In the parallel circuit, there is another loop for the current to flow through *[1 mark]*. As there is only one resistor in each loop it is no harder for the current to flow in each loop as in the series circuit *[1 mark]*. This means that the total current increases *[1 mark]* and so the total resistance must decrease *[1 mark]*.

2   How to grade your answer:

Level 0: There is no relevant information. *[No marks]*

Level 1: There is a brief description of the method used to measure resistance of the circuit. The steps mentioned are not in a logical order. *[1 to 2 marks]*

Level 2: There is a good description of the method used to measure the resistance of the circuit. Most steps are given in a logical order. A correct circuit diagram may be included. *[3 to 4 marks]*

Level 3: A logical and detailed description of the method used to measure the resistance of the circuit is given. The method for investigating the effect of adding resistors in parallel is fully described. A correct circuit diagram may be included. *[5 to 6 marks]*

Here are some points your answer may include:
Assume the potential difference across the resistor is the same as the potential difference across the battery.
Measure the current through the circuit using the ammeter.
Calculate the resistance of the circuit using $R = V \div I$.
Connect a second identical resistor in parallel with the first resistor.
The second resistor should not be in parallel with the ammeter.
Measure the current and use this to calculate the resistance of the circuit.
Repeat this for several identical resistors.
A correct circuit diagram, similar to:

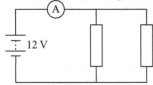

A correct diagram with at least two resistors in parallel is correct. You could also draw your circuit with several resistors in parallel, all separated with switches.

Page 185 — Energy in Circuits

Warm-up
To toast a slice of bread a toaster transfers energy.
Energy is transferred from the a.c. mains supply to the thermal energy stores of the toaster's heating coils **electrically**. Energy is then transferred **by heating** to the **thermal** energy stores of the bread and the **surroundings**.

1   C *[1 mark]*

2 a) Energy transferred = current × potential difference × time
so, current = energy transferred ÷
        (potential difference × time)
      = 48 300 ÷ (230 × 30)
      = **7.0 A**
[3 marks for correct answer, otherwise 1 mark for correct rearrangement and 1 mark for correct substitution]

  b) E.g. it causes fuses to melt, which can be used to protect circuits *[1 mark]*.

Page 186 — Electrical Power

1 a) electrical power = current × potential difference
              = 6 × 2 = **12 W**
[2 mark for correct answer, otherwise 1 mark for correct substitution]

  b) power = energy transferred ÷ time taken *[1 mark]*

  c) Rearrange the equation for energy transferred:
energy transferred = power × time taken
energy transferred = 12 × 30 = 360 J
[3 marks for correct answer, otherwise 1 mark for correct rearrangement and 1 mark for correct substitution]

2   electrical power = current squared × resistance
so, current = $\sqrt{\text{electrical power} \div \text{resistance}}$
current = $\sqrt{1250 \div 8.0}$ = **12.5 A**
[3 marks for correct answer, otherwise 1 mark for correct rearrangement and 1 mark for correct substitution]

Page 187 — Electricity in the Home

Warm-up
The type of current supplied by a battery — Direct current
The type of current where the direction of movement of the charge is in one direction
    — Direct current
The type of current supplied by the UK domestic supply
    — Alternating current
The type of current where the direction of movement of the charge changes direction
    — Alternating current

1 a) Voltage: 230 V *[1 mark]*
Frequency: 50 Hz *[1 mark]*

  b) i) A direct voltage means the potential difference is only ever positive or negative, not both *[1 mark]*. However, with an alternating voltage, the positive and negative ends of the potential difference alternate *[1 mark]*.

    ii)

Wires	Potential difference / V
Live wire and neutral wire	230
Neutral wire and earth wire	0
Earth wire and live wire	230

[3 marks — 1 mark for each correct answer]

Page 188 — Electrical Safety

1   live wire *[1 mark]*

2   There is a potential difference between the live wire and your body *[1 mark]*. Touching it could cause a current to flow through you to the Earth *[1 mark]*. This will result in an electric shock *[1 mark]*.

3 a) The large current melts the thin wire in the fuse *[1 mark]*, which breaks the circuit so no current can flow *[1 mark]*.

  b) To protect the wiring in the house *[1 mark]*.

  c) Circuit breakers *[1 mark]*.

Page 189 — Transformers and the National Grid

1   B *[1 mark]*

2 a) Step-up transformers increase the voltage before transmission *[1 mark]*. Step-down transformers lower the voltage for domestic use by the consumer *[1 mark]*.

   b) For a given power, increasing the potential difference decreases the current *[1 mark]*. Transmitting electricity with a high current heats the wires, which leads to energy loss by heating *[1 mark]*. So transmitting electricity at a high p.d. is an efficient way of transferring energy as it reduces the energy lost from heating *[1 mark]*.

3     $V_p \times I_p = V_s \times I_s$
     so $I_p = (V_s \times I_s) \div V_p$
     $I_p = (240 \times 0.5) \div 20$
         $= \mathbf{6\,A}$

     [3 marks for correct answer, otherwise 1 mark for correct rearrangement and 1 mark for correct substitution]

Section 23 — Magnetic Fields

Page 190 — Magnets and Magnetic Fields

Warm-up

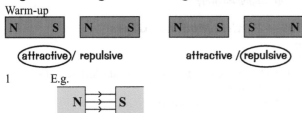

(attractive)/ repulsive   attractive /(repulsive)

1   E.g.

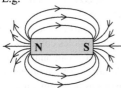

     [1 mark for at least three straight, evenly spaced field lines and 1 mark for at least one arrow in the right direction with no arrows in the wrong direction]

2 a) E.g.

     [1 mark for at least three lines showing the correct shape of the field, 1 mark for at least one arrow going from north to south with no arrows in the incorrect direction]

   b) They would be closer together / there would be more lines in a given area *[1 mark]*.

Page 191 — Permanent and Induced Magnets

1   E.g. iron / nickel / cobalt
     [2 marks — 1 mark for each correct answer]

2 a) E.g. a permanent magnet produces its own magnetic field at all times *[1 mark]*. An induced magnet only produces a magnetic field because it is placed in another magnetic field *[1 mark]*.

   b) E.g. magnetic strips in fridges are used to hold the door of the fridge closed *[1 mark]*.

3 a) The block of cobalt has become an induced magnet *[1 mark]*.

   b) When the bar magnet is removed, the cobalt will stop being a magnet *[1 mark]*, so the paperclip will become unstuck *[1 mark]*.

Page 192 — Electromagnetism and Solenoids

1 a) A solenoid with a current flowing through it is an example of an electromagnet. Outside of the solenoid, the field lines of each coil cancel out to create a weaker magnetic field than inside the solenoid. *[3 marks — 1 mark for each correct answer]*

   b) E.g. a plotting compass *[1 mark]*

2 a) E.g.

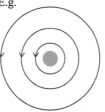

     [1 mark for correct shape of magnetic field lines, 1 mark for an arrow on each field line pointing in the anticlockwise direction]

   b) B *[1 mark]*

   c) The magnetic field gets stronger *[1 mark]* and its direction reverses *[1 mark]*.

Section 24 — Matter

Page 193 — Density

1   B *[1 mark]*

2   E.g. place the empty cylinder on the balance and zero the balance *[1 mark]*. Then pour a known volume of acid into the cylinder *[1 mark]* and write down the mass of the acid shown on the balance *[1 mark]*. Use the equation density = mass ÷ volume to calculate the density of the acid *[1 mark]*.

3 a) C *[1 mark]*

   b) volume = mass ÷ density
          = 7720 ÷ 19 300 = **0.4 m³**
     [2 marks for correct answer, otherwise 1 mark for correct substitution]

   c) mass = volume × density
          = 0.12 × 19 300
          = 2316
          = **2300 kg (to 2 s.f.)**
     [3 marks for correct answer, otherwise 1 mark for correct rearrangement and 1 mark for correct substitution]

Page 194 — Kinetic Theory and States of Matter

Warm-up

From left to right: liquid, solid, gas

1 a) Melting: (A substance changing from a) solid to a liquid
     Freezing: (A substance changing from a) liquid to a solid
     Condensing: (A substance changing from a) gas to a liquid
     [3 marks — 1 mark for each correct answer]

   b) A physical change is different to a chemical change. If you reverse a physical change, the substance will get back its original properties. *[2 marks — 1 mark for each correct answer]*.

2   10 g *[1 mark]* e.g. because the total mass stays the same as a change of state is a physical change *[1 mark]*.

Pages 195-196 — Specific Heat Capacity

1 a) The amount of energy needed to raise the temperature of 1 kg of the substance by 1 °C *[1 mark]*.

 b) Materials with high specific heat capacities are good **thermal** insulators. They can be used to **reduce** energy transfers by heating.
 [2 marks — 1 mark for each correct answer]

2 a) First convert 200 g into kg:
 200 ÷ 1000 = 0.2 kg
 Then rearrange the equation $\Delta Q = m \times c \times \Delta\theta$
 for the specific heat capacity:
 $c = \Delta Q \div (m \times \Delta\theta)$
 $= 9000 \div (0.2 \times 50)$
 = **900 J/kg°C**
 [3 marks for correct answer, otherwise 1 mark for correct rearrangement and 1 mark for correct conversion and substitution]

 b) E.g. as the aluminium is heated, energy is transferred to the kinetic energy stores of the aluminium particles *[1 mark]*. In kinetic theory, temperature is a measure of the average energy in the kinetic energy stores of a substance's particles *[1 mark]*. So increasing the energy in the aluminium particles' kinetic energy stores leads to an increase in the temperature of the aluminium *[1 mark]*.

3 a) Ticks should be placed in the following columns:
 The mass of the block — Control variable *[1 mark]*
 The change in temperature of the block —
 Dependent variable *[1 mark]*
 The temperature of the room — Control variable *[1 mark]*

 b) i) systematic error *[1 mark]*
 ii) Subtract 1 °C from all the measurements / repeat the experiment and retake all the readings correctly *[1 mark]*.

 c) mean temperature = (31.0 + 29.5 + 32.5) ÷ 3 *[1 mark]*
 = 31.0 °C *[1 mark]*

Page 197 — Specific Latent Heat

Warm-up
The energy needed to change the state of 1 kg of a substance without changing its temperature.

1 E.g. specific heat capacity is the energy needed to cause a temperature rise without causing a change of state *[1 mark]*, but specific latent heat is the energy needed to cause a change of state, where the temperature remains constant *[1 mark]*.

2 a) Convert kJ to J:
 183.7 × 1000 = 183 700 J
 $Q = m \times L$, so $m = Q \div L$
 $m = 183\,700 \div 334\,000$ = **0.55 kg**
 [3 marks for correct answer, otherwise 1 mark for correct rearrangement and 1 mark for correct conversion and substitution]

 b) $Q = m \times L$
 $= 0.55 \times 2\,260\,000$
 $= 1\,243\,000$
 = **1 200 000 J (to 2 s.f.)**
 [3 marks for correct answer, otherwise 1 mark for correct substitution and 1 mark for correct unrounded answer]

Page 198 — Investigating Water

1 a) It is melting *[1 mark]*.
 b) 8 minutes *[1 mark]*
 After the ice has melted, the temperature of the water increases. This is shown by the line between 4 and 8 minutes on the graph. The flat section from 8 minutes onwards shows the time during which the water is boiling.

2 a) Trial 3 is an anomalous result, so it shouldn't be used to calculate the average.
 Average = (11.9 + 12.2 + 11.9 + 12.0) ÷ 4 = **12.0**
 [2 marks for correct answer, otherwise 1 mark for recognising anomalous result and not including it in the average calculation]

 b) Convert g to kg:
 60 ÷ 1000 = 0.06 kg
 specific heat capacity = change in thermal energy
 ÷ (mass × change in temperature)
 = 3050 ÷ (0.06 × 12.0)
 = 4236.11...
 = **4200 J/kg°C (to 2 s.f.)**
 [3 marks for correct answer, otherwise 1 mark for conversion and substitution and 1 mark for correct unrounded answer]

Page 199 — Particle Motion in Gases

Warm-up
−273 °C

1 E.g. absolute zero is the temperature at which particles barely move *[1 mark]*.

2 155 + 273 = 428 K *[1 mark]*

3 a) E.g. the particles in a gas are free to move around and collide with the walls of the container that they're in *[1 mark]*. When they hit the container walls, they exert a force on them *[1 mark]*. Pressure is the force over a given area, so the gas particles exert a pressure on the container walls *[1 mark]*.

 b) Heating a gas transfers energy to the kinetic energy stores of its particles, which causes the particles to move faster *[1 mark]*. This means that the particles collide with the container walls more often in a given amount of time *[1 mark]*. This increases the force exerted on the container walls, so the pressure increases as the temperature of the gas increases *[1 mark]*.

Page 200 — Forces and Elasticity

1 C *[1 mark]*

2 force exerted on a spring = spring constant × extension
 = 250 × 0.08 = **20 N**
 [2 marks for correct answer, otherwise 1 mark for correct substitution]

3 a) One force would just make the spring move, not change shape *[1 mark]*.

 b) An object that has been elastically distorted will go back to its original shape and length when the distorting forces are removed *[1 mark]*. An object that has been inelastically distorted won't *[1 mark]*.

Answers

Page 201 — Investigating Elasticity

1 a)

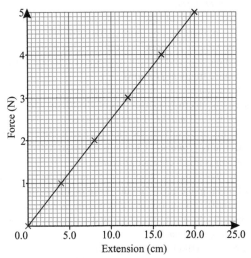

[2 marks for 3 points plotted correctly, otherwise 1 mark for 1 or 2 points plotted correctly. 1 mark for correct line of best fit.]

b) From the graph, the force causing an extension of 10.0 cm is 2.5 N.

The work done by this force is equal to the area under the line for a force of 2.5 N.

First, convert 10.0 cm to m:

$10.0 \div 100 = 0.10$ m

Then, calculate the area under the line (which is the area of a triangle):

Area of triangle = ½ × base × height
= ½ × 0.10 × 2.5
= 0.125

So the work done = **0.125 J**

[3 marks for correct answer, otherwise 1 mark for reading force value from graph correctly and 1 mark for a correct method for finding the area under the line, including any conversions]

You could also use the counting the squares method to find the area under the line.

2 Convert 120 mm into m:

$120 \div 1000 = 0.12$ m

$E = \frac{1}{2} \times k \times x^2$

so $k = E \div (\frac{1}{2} \times x^2)$
$= 0.18 \div (\frac{1}{2} \times 0.12^2)$
= **25 N/m**

[3 marks for correct answer, otherwise 1 mark for correct rearrangement and 1 mark for correct conversion and substitution]

Mixed Questions

Pages 202-206 — Biology Mixed Questions

1 a) C *[1 mark]*
  b) C *[1 mark]*
  c) E.g. it has got a nucleus / it doesn't have any plasmids / it doesn't have a long circular strand of DNA *[1 mark]*.
  d) D *[1 mark]*
2 a) B *[1 mark]*
  b) The concentration of glucose in the blood *[1 mark]*.
  c) A *[1 mark]*
3 a) i) mitochondria *[1 mark]*
    ii) glucose + **oxygen** *[1 mark]* → **carbon dioxide** *[1 mark]* + water
  b) plasma *[1 mark]*
  c) E.g. obesity / a high BMI / a high waist-to-hip ratio *[1 mark]*
4 a) photosynthesis *[1 mark]*
The reactants of photosynthesis (carbon dioxide and water) are going into the sub-cellular structure and the products of photosynthesis (glucose and oxygen) are leaving it — this suggests that photosynthesis is happening inside the sub-cellular structure.
  b) chloroplast *[1 mark]*
  c) A *[1 mark]*
Remember, 1 mm = 1000 µm, so 45 mm will equal 45 000 µm.
  d) Water evaporates and diffuses out of a leaf *[1 mark]*, through the stomata *[1 mark]*.
  e) transpiration *[1 mark]*
  f) translocation *[1 mark]*
5 a) A *[1 mark]*
  b) 9 *[1 mark]*
  c) The enzyme will not work *[1 mark]* because the acid will change the shape of its active site/denature the enzyme *[1 mark]* and the substrate will no longer fit *[1 mark]*.
  d) C *[1 mark]*
6 a) Any two from: e.g. light intensity / levels of pollutants / temperature / amount of water *[2 marks — 1 mark for each correct answer]*.
  b) The number of mice may decrease *[1 mark]* because there would be more snakes eating them *[1 mark]*.
  c) E.g. the population of snakes may decrease *[1 mark]* because they would be competing with the owls for mice/food *[1 mark]*.
  d) E.g. the scientist could mark out a transect line across the ecosystem *[1 mark]*. He/she could then place quadrats along the line *[1 mark]* and count the number of buttercups in each quadrat *[1 mark]*.
  e) In a parasitic relationship, the parasite benefits from the host, but the host does not get any benefit from the parasite *[1 mark]*.
  f) The mass of living material *[1 mark]*.

34

Pages 207-213 — Chemistry Mixed Questions

1 a) lithium *[1 mark]*
b) Any one from: sodium / potassium / rubidium / caesium / francium *[1 mark]*
c)
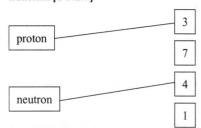

[2 marks — 1 mark for each correct line]

d)

[1 mark]

e) When a Group 1 element reacts with water a metal **hydroxide** *[1 mark]* is formed.

2 a) mean = (35.60 + 35.90 + 35.75) ÷ 3 = **35.75 cm³** *[2 marks for correct answer, otherwise 1 mark for correct method]*
b) range = 35.90 − 35.60 = 0.30
uncertainty = 0.30 ÷ 2 = **0.15 cm³** *[2 marks for correct answer, otherwise 1 mark for calculating range]*
c) $HCl + NaOH \rightarrow NaCl + H_2O$ *[1 mark for HCl, 1 mark for NaCl]*
d) E.g. the pH would start high/above pH 7 *[1 mark]*. As the hydrochloric acid is added it would decrease *[1 mark]* until it reached pH 7/falls below pH 7 *[1 mark]*.
e)
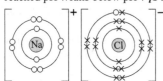

[1 mark for adding seven crosses and one dot to outer shell of Cl⁻ ion, 1 mark for correct charge on both ions]
f) ionic *[1 mark]*

3 a)

	Higher boiling points	Easier to ignite	More viscous
Short hydrocarbons		✓	
Long hydrocarbons	✓		✓

[3 marks — 1 mark for each correct answer]

b) carbon dioxide *[1 mark]*
c) e.g. hydrogen gas *[1 mark]*

4 a)

[1 mark for shared pair of electrons, 1 mark for six further electrons in the outer shell of each chlorine atom]

b) C *[1 mark]*
c) Hold a piece of damp litmus paper in the unknown gas *[1 mark]*. It will be bleached white in the presence of chlorine *[1 mark]*.

5 a) Group: 6 *[1 mark]*
Explanation: There are 6 electrons in the outer shell *[1 mark]*.
b) Charge: 2− *[1 mark]*
Reason: Oxygen atoms need to gain two electrons to get a full outer shell *[1 mark]*.

6 a) hydrogen/H_2 *[1 mark]*
b) Reaction D *[1 mark]*. The most reactive metal will react fastest with the acid *[1 mark]*. In reaction D the largest volume of gas has been collected in the syringe / the most bubbles are being given off *[1 mark]*.
c) A *[1 mark]*

7 a) endothermic *[1 mark]*
b) higher *[1 mark]*
c) Effect: the rate of reaction will increase *[1 mark]*.
Reason: there will be more particles of ethanoic acid in the same volume *[1 mark]* so collisions between the reactant/ethanoic acid and sodium hydrogen carbonate particles will be more frequent *[1 mark]*.

8 a) Extraction process: electrolysis *[1 mark]*
Reason: electrolysis uses lots of electricity which is expensive *[1 mark]*. There are also costs associated with melting or dissolving the metal ore so it can conduct electricity *[1 mark]*. Carbon is cheap so reduction with carbon is much cheaper *[1 mark]*.
b) Any two from: e.g. it helps save some of the finite amount of metal in the earth / it cuts down on the waste getting sent to landfill / it's good for the economy as it creates jobs / it prevents the environment being damaged by mining for new metal ores *[2 marks]*.

9 a) a piece of (filter) paper *[1 mark]*
b) R_f of **A** = 4.6 ÷ 12.1 = **0.38** *[1 mark]*
R_f of **B** = 10.6 ÷ 12.1 = **0.88** *[1 mark]*
c) There is a spot of substance on the baseline / there is a substance with an R_f value of 0 *[1 mark]*.
d) A mixture is a substance that contains more than one compound or more than one element that aren't all part of a single compound *[1 mark]*.
e) E.g. fractional distillation *[1 mark]*

10 a) water *[1 mark]*
b) $ZnCl_2$ *[1 mark]*
c) Filter the solution to remove the excess solid zinc oxide *[1 mark]*, then heat the solution and allow some of the water to evaporate *[1 mark]*. Leave the solution to cool until crystals form *[1 mark]*. Filter the crystals from the remaining solution and allow them to dry *[1 mark]*.

11 How to grade your answer:
Level 0: There is no relevant information. *[No marks]*
Level 1: A brief attempt is made to explain one or two of the properties in terms of structure and/or bonding. *[1 to 2 marks]*
Level 2: Some explanation of all three properties, in terms of structure and/or bonding, is given, or a complete explanation of one or two of these properties is given. *[3 to 4 marks]*
Level 3: Clear and detailed explanation of all three properties, in terms of both structure and bonding, is given. *[5 to 6 marks]*

Here are some points your answer may include:
Diamond
Each carbon atom in diamond forms four covalent bonds in a rigid giant covalent structure, making it very hard.
Because it is made up of lots of covalent bonds, which take a lot of energy to break, diamond has a very high melting point.
There are no free/delocalised electrons in the structure of diamond, so it can't conduct electricity.
Graphite
Each carbon atom in graphite forms three covalent bonds.
The carbon atoms are arranged in layers of hexagons.
There are no covalent bonds between layers, so the layers can slide over each other.
This makes graphite soft and slippery.
The covalent bonds between the carbon atoms take a lot of energy to break, giving graphite a very high melting point.
Each carbon atom has one electron which is free to move, so graphite has lots of free/delocalised electrons and can conduct electricity.

Answers